THE TEA COUNCIL'S
BEST TEA PLACES

2000/2001

Published by
The Tea Council Ltd
No. 9, The Courtyard
Gowan Avenue
London
SW6 6RH

Compiled by: Jane Pettigrew,
Anita Crocker

Design and origination by Roger Simmons Design
Consultancy Limited, The Studio, Entry Hill, Bath BA2 5LY
Printed by Harlequin Colourprint Ltd, Bristol BS4 5QW

Contents

A member of The Tea Council

The Tea Council

Guild of Tea Shops

FOREWORD

Tea is Britain's No. 1 drink. It is a natural healthy beverage, which cools, calms and refreshes. Some 144 million cups of tea slide down British throats daily, with more than three quarters of the nation imbibing tea every day of their lives. We have been enjoying a love affair with tea for more than 300 years. It has had a remarkable influence on the British social, cultural, industrial and economic development. Today, afternoon tea is a major tourist attraction for visitors to our shores. Tea is served in tea shops, tea rooms, restaurants, cafes and hotel lounges throughout the nation.

As a nation of tea drinkers, who all consider themselves expert brewers, we have very high standards when taking tea out of the home. To take account of this, The Tea Council founded The Guild of Tea Shops and began publishing its guide to the Best Tea Places.

Within the covers of this book you will find notes about tea — its history; growth and manufacture; health benefits of drinking tea and how by pairing specific teas with various dishes or foods,

you can enhance the enjoyment and digestion of a meal, be it lunch, afternoon tea or dinner.

Some of the best tea places in Britain, to suit all tastes and pockets, are listed in the guide. All are members of the The Guild of Tea Shops, invited by The Tea Council to join the Guild and inspected annually by a professional tea taster.

There is nothing more relaxing and enjoyable than a good tea served in a tea shop, tea room or hotel tea lounge, whether you are out shopping, walking, driving or just meeting a friend for a chat. Remember many of the tea shops and tea rooms serve delicious lunches and our panel of professional tea tasters sample the food served in Guild member outlets as part of their inspection criteria.

For readers who travel abroad, either for business or pleasure, The Tea Council has inaugurated a list of 'honorary' overseas members, who are known to serve good quality tea made and served properly, so that you can enjoy a little home from home when abroad.

Enjoy your tea.

Illtyd Lewis
Executive Director, The Tea Council Ltd

THE GUILD OF TEA SHOPS AND ITS RATIONALE

Tea, our national drink, is served in thousands of outlets across Britain on a daily basis. An independent study commissioned by The Tea Council revealed that very few of these outlets were serving tea to the high standards that The Tea Council believes desirable.

Therefore The Tea Council concluded that recognition should be given only to those establishments which fulfil their exacting criteria and meet their high standards in serving, selling and preparing tea. This recognition is given by invitation to membership of the unique and prestigious organisation – The Tea Council's Guild of Tea Shops.

Membership is limited to one hundred outlets. All establishments must first pass an exacting and incognito inspection by acknowledged tea tasters. Once a shop has become a member, The Tea Council maintains a watching brief on Guild members throughout the year to ensure standards of excellence.

If you know of a tea shop which you think should be a member of The Guild, please write in with the name, address and reason you liked it, and we will be sure to investigate.

Each tea place featured in this guide offers you a pleasant, relaxing and reviving experience at a price which gives good value for money. The Guild of Tea Shops endorses high standards of tea making and serving, home baking, cleanliness and hygiene, staff efficiency and attitude.

Some of the Guild member shops operate a no smoking policy which is represented by the symbol ⊛. ♿ represents wheelchair access. Both symbols are displayed under the opening times of the tea shops.

COME RAIN OR SHINE: TEA IS BRITAIN'S FIRST CHOICE

The British have been drinking tea for more than three hundred years. Today, tea accounts for 41% of everything we drink and 75% of the population drink tea daily. We import about 16% of the producer countries' exports and Britain is a major buyer in the world tea market. In fact, we import more tea than the whole of Europe and North America combined.

A staggering 185 million cups of tea a day are drunk in Britain. By the time British tea drinkers reach the ripe old age of 'three score years and ten', we shall each have drunk an estimated 90,000 cups of tea. So we drink 8.23 units of fluid per person per day (a unit being 7 fluid ounces). Statistically tea accounts for 3.39 units, coffee 1.65 units, alcohol 1.38 units, soft drinks 1.51 units and others 0.3 units a day.

Tea has influenced our history, culture and society. The growth of the British potteries and the ship building industry are indebted to tea. In the second half of the eighteenth century, British potteries such as Spode, Worcester, Derby and Wedgwood were producing tea wares. In 1850, the first British clipper, *The Stornaway*, was built in Aberdeen. These new, faster ships cut the journey time radically from China to British shores. The *Cutty Sark* is one of our famous clippers. Many of our famous authors and poets have written hundreds of lines describing the nation's favourite drink: Samuel Pepys, Dr Johnson, Lewis Carroll, Noel Coward to name just a few. Our nation's leaders have always relied on the virtues of tea. Wellington, while fighting at Waterloo, was said to stop for a quick cup while encouraging his troops to victory. Gladstone is reputed to have filled his hot water bottle with tea enabling him both to warm his feet and quench his thirst throughout the night.

A POTTED HISTORY OF TEA

Tea is indigenous to both China and India, and both countries tell their own legends about the discovery of the plant. China's Shen Nung, often referred to as an emperor, is said to have been boiling some water under a tree one day when some leaves from an overhanging branch fell into the pot. He smelt the tea's aroma, tasted the brew and liked it. By the time of the Tang Dynasty (906–618 BC) tea was popular throughout China. Until the name 'tea' became accepted into the English language, the leaf and beverage were variously called tcha, cha, tay and tee. 'Cha' derives from the Mandarin Chinese word 'cha', and tea from the Chinese Amoy dialect name 'te'.

Buddhist monks are reputed to have spread the tea drinking habit around the East by cultivating tea gardens in the grounds of monasteries and royal palaces. In the early 800s AD, a Japanese monk took the first tea seeds from China to his native country where they were used to establish Japan's first plantation. Tea's popularity spread rapidly around Japan where the early Chinese method of whisking powdered tea into hot water developed into the famous Japanese Green Tea Ceremony.

According to the American author, William Ukers, Hajji Mahommed, a Persian merchant, brought the first knowledge of tea to Europe. He described his travels in Cathay to the Venetian traveller, Giambattista Ramusio who wrote that Mahommed claimed people "made use of another plant or rather its leaves. This is called Chai Catai and grows in the district of Cathay, which is called Caican-fu (Szechwan)". In 1559, Ramusio published Volume 11 of his *Navigatione et Viaggi* in which he described how tea was made and drunk by the residents of Cathay.

The Portuguese and the Dutch are credited with the spread of tea drinking and trading in Europe in the late sixteenth and early seventeenth centuries. By 1557, the Portuguese had established a trading base at Macao, although tea was not at first amongst the items shipped out of China. The Dutch started sending regular consignments of China tea from their base on the island of Java in 1606 and so Europe gradually became familiar with the herb. By this time, the British East India Company had opened up trading routes to the East, but concentrated not on tea but on spices and silks. However, in 1615, an agent of the company who was based on the Japanese island of Hirado wrote to a colleague at Macao asking him to forward a pot of 'the best sort of chaw'. But there is no evidence of tea being generally available in England until 1657 when Thomas Garraway claimed that he had started to sell 'the leaf and drink'. Garraway owned a popular coffee house in Exchange Alley in the City of London (a blue plaque still marks the spot today) and in 1660, published a broadsheet extolling the virtues of the beverage and its health benefits. And in 1658, the London newspaper, *Mercurius Politicus*, had published the first advertisement for the sale of tea by auction at the Sultaness Head Coffee House, Sweetings Rents by the Royal Exchange in London. So the fashion for drinking tea began in the coffee houses of London – the forerunners of gentlemen's clubs. The popularity of the new beverage increased when the Portuguese princess, Catherine of Braganza, arrived in England to marry Charles 11 in 1662 and brought with her a 3lb chest of tea as part of her dowry. She served tea to her friends at court and so awareness and demand slowly grew. Gradually, the drink that was so fashionable amongst the rich and famous became the favourite drink of the entire population.

Throughout the seventeenth and the greater part of the eighteenth centuries, tea was extremely expensive, at first because it was a rare commodity, but also because it was very heavily taxed. This meant that the family's supply was locked away in caddies that were kept under the watchful eye of the lady of the house, servants were paid part of their wages in tea, and leaves were often brewed several times in order not to waste any of the precious flavour.

The high cost led to the smuggling of tea from Holland and France, the adulteration of genuine tea with the leaves of other plants, and a thriving black market. These practices continued until 1784 when William Pitt the Younger, the then Prime Minister, had the Commutation law passed by Parliament to reduce the tax on tea from 119% to 12.5%.

It was tea taxes too that led to the serious eighteenth century rift between Britain and America. The East India Company had their charter, granted by Elizabeth I, revised twice. In 1669, it was granted the British trading monopoly in the East and imports from Holland were banned. The Tea Act of 1773 further revised the charter, giving the company monopoly of British trading with China and India, plus import rights in the colonies. British subjects in the colonies were forced to pay the same import duties as the British. This resulted in the Boston Tea Party and culminated in the War of Independence.

By the middle of the eighteenth century in Britain, the coffee houses had disappeared and the pleasure gardens of London had taken their place as centres of entertainment, social life and tea drinking. The charge for entrance to such fashionable gardens as Ranelagh in Chelsea, Marylebone and Vauxhall included tea with bread and butter – welcome refreshment after firework displays, concerts, boat rides, promenades, bowling and gambling. But rapid urban growth at the beginning of the nineteenth century led to the closure of the gardens and the only places serving tea (or coffee) as well as alcohol were inns, taverns and hostelries. In fact, tea played an important part in the temperence movement's battle against high levels of alcohol consumption and tea meetings were held all over Britain in an attempt to convert drinkers and to raise money for the cause. It is possible that the word 't-total' has close connections with the beverage.

For the first 180 years of tea drinking in Britain, almost all the tea drunk was imported from China (with Japan, the only tea producing area at the time). Both green and black teas were taken with milk (or cream) and sugar, and despite the high cost, even the poorest families drank tea at least three times a day, including with their main meal. In the late 1830s, British plantations were established in India and the 1870s saw the growth of production in Ceylon, now Sri Lanka. This meant that prices gradually became cheaper and consumption increased, although imports from China dropped.

In 1864, London's first public tearoom opened when the manageress of the London Bridge branch of the Aerated Bread Company asked her directors if she could use a spare room to serve tea to customers when they called in for their bread and cakes. The success of this pioneering tearoom led to the creation of many more by other companies, and by the turn of the century, going out to tea had become an essential part of British social life.

AFTERNOON TEA

When tea was first introduced to Britain, it was advertised and drunk as a tonic that was thought to be good for such ailments as colds, skin complaints, stomach disorders, and depression. But it quickly became a popular drink that was enjoyed more for its taste and refreshing properties than for its medicinal qualities. It began to replace ale and beer at breakfast, was drunk at all times of the day and became so widely popular that in 1699, the Revd. Ovington wrote in his *Essay upon the Nature and Qualities of Tea*, "...the drinking of it has of late obtained here so universally, as to be affected both by the Scholar and the tradesman, to become both a private regale at court, and to be made use of in places of public entertainment"

Throughout the eighteenth century, as well as drinking tea at breakfast with bread and butter, it was common practice in wealthier households to take tea after the main meal of the day. At the beginning of the century, this was served at noon or one o'clock and could last for anything up to four or five hours. For the final two hours or so of this time, the ladies withdrew to a boudoir or small drawing room while the gentlemen drank port and wine, smoked cigars and talked. A servant would then announce that tea was ready and the men would join the ladies for tea and a game or two of whist. A light supper of cold meat, perhaps a hot dish and biscuits or toast was sometimes served to guests before they left for home. So the idea of serving tea at some appropriate point in the afternoon or early evening was firmly established as part of the day's activities. As social patterns changed, dinner was served gradually later and later in the day until, by the beginning of the nineteenth century, it was at 8 or 9 o'clock in the evening. This left a rather long gap between breakfast at 9.30 am and the evening meal, and so ladies like Anna

Maria, 7th Duchess of Bedford, whose country home was Woburn Abbey, needed some extra nourishment in the middle of the afternoon to stave off what she called a "sinking feeling". She is said to have asked her maid to bring her a pot of tea with some bread and butter (or other light refreshment) to her private boudoir and is said to have enjoyed it so much that she started inviting her friends to join her for what she called 'afternoon tea'.

The Victorian period was tea's heyday. Tea parties were created for every possible social occasion. High tea, with its filling savoury dishes, home-baked breads, cheeses, cakes and puddings, was the hearty meal that fed hungry working class families at the end of long shifts in mills, mines, offices and shops, and it was always a large pot of tea that accompanied the food. Because high tea often included a meat dish of some kind, it was also called 'meat tea' or 'great tea'. Afternoon tea, on the other hand, was referred to as 'little tea' or 'low tea' because those taking it sat in low armchairs and sofas and had small tables at their side on which to place cups and saucers. 'At Home' receptions gave society ladies the opportunity to receive up to two hundred guests to an afternoon buffet with cups of tea handed round by the servants. Cheap travel on steam trains allowed town dwellers to escape into the country for a picnic tea by a river or in the corner of a field. Children at the top of upper middle class and aristocratic houses took nursery tea every day with their nanny or governess. Tea in the garden of stately homes and manor houses was served with all the same fine porcelains and fancy linen and lace cloths that were used inside the house. Ladies gathered over their sewing or bridge games and always included tea in the afternoon's agenda. And by the 1880s, fashion designers were creating breathtakingly beautiful tea gowns of silks and satins, chiffon, lace and velvet, in which fine ladies draped themselves on chaises longues and armchairs and took tea with their friends. The idea of these flowing robes was to allow a lady to remove her cripplingly tight corsets, breathe freely and enjoy her afternoon tea while still looking incredibly stylish and feminine.

By the end of the nineteenth century, cookery and etiquette books were instructing ladies and housekeepers as to when and how to serve tea, when and how to invite friends, the duties of the servants, what food to offer, how to brew the tea, and how to organise different tea events. The simple slices or rolls of bread and butter of the early part of the century were replaced by neat sandwiches (always with the crusts cut off), scones and muffins, biscuits, cakes and pastries. And the brewing of the tea was still carried out in the drawing room by the lady of the house, just as it had always been ever since tea first arrived in the middle of the seventeenth century. A small table was placed close to the hostess with cups and saucers, the kettle, one or two tea pots (sometimes different types of tea were offered), little side plates, milk, sugar and silver teaspoons. She would then pour the tea for her guests while her daughters or a maid offered the plates of food.

In the Edwardian period, afternoon tea was a feature in many of the new hotels that opened and palm court trios and string quartets entertained guests while they relaxed over a cup of Darjeeling or Ceylon. And teashops around the country attracted people of all types and all ages whose orders were delivered to their table by efficient black and white clad waitresses. The arrival of the tango from Argentina in 1910 led to the eccentric craze for tango tea dances from 1913 to the early 1920s. But two world wars and the 1950s coffee bar and fast food revolution changed British life and pushed tea out of the limelight for a short while. However, since the early 1980s, tearooms and tea generally have been enjoying a renaissance, not just in Britain but around the world, and taking tea in the afternoon is as fashionable as it ever was in Victorian and Edwardian days.

BREWING A GOOD CUP OF TEA

- Use good quality loose leaf or bagged tea
- Always use freshly drawn boiling water (except for green tea, when the boiled water should be allowed to cool a little first)
- Measure the tea carefully: use one tea bag or one rounded teaspoon of loose tea for each cup to be served
- Allow the tea to brew for two to five minutes before pouring. Technically allowing the infusion to last for five minutes extracts the very best from the tea. However brewing time is a matter of personal choice

TEA	COUNTRY OF ORIGIN	MILK/BLACK/ LEMON*	CHARACTERISTICS
DARJEELING	INDIA	BLACK or MILK	Delicate, slightly astringent flavour
ASSAM	INDIA	BLACK or MILK	Full-bodied with a rich, smooth, malty flavour
CEYLON BLEND	SRI LANKA	BLACK or MILK	Brisk, full flavour with a bright colour
KENYA	KENYA	BLACK or MILK	A strong tea with a brisk flavour
EARL GREY	CHINA OR INDIA	BLACK or LEMON	Flavoured with the natural oil of citrus bergamot fruit
LAPSANG SOUCHONG	CHINA	BLACK	Smoky aroma and flavour
CHINA OOLONG	CHINA	BLACK	Subtle, delicate, lightly flavoured tea

*The addition of lemon is a matter of personal choice.

A PROFILE OF TEA

Tea – an evergreen plant – is a member of the Camellia family, known botanically as Camellia Sinensis.

The characteristics and flavour of tea will vary according to the soil, altitude and climatic conditions of the areas in which it is grown. Other contributory factors are the methods by which tea is processed and, of course, the blending together of teas from different growing areas. Today, there is a choice of some 1,500 tea blends which are grown in more than 31 countries.

TEA CULTIVATION

In the wild tea grows as a tree, reaching a height of some 10 metres. Today, under modern cultivation, tea is kept to bush size – approximately 1.5 metres high – and planted in rows roughly 1.5 metres apart. Bushes are trained to grow in a "fan shape" with a flat oblong top – known in the tea trade as a plucking plateau – 1 x 1.5 metres big. The rows, planted 1 metre apart for easy access by the pluckers, form continuous tea "hedges"

and, when grown on hill and mountainsides, are planted around the contours of the land to avoid soil erosion. Leaves are only plucked from the plucking plateau. A fine pluck – the best pluck – comprises the top two leaves and a bud, as against coarse pluck – the top four leaves and a bud. After plucking, tea renews itself – rather like the British privet hedge – every 7 to 14 days, depending on the altitude and climatic conditions of the area in which it is growing.

TEA "MAKING" PROCESSES

When tea trade people talk about "making tea" they are referring to the processing of the plucked leaf. There are three types of tea "makes" black, oolong and green.

BLACK TEA comprises the largest percentage of the worldwide tea market and there are five stages in its manufacture.

1. *Withering.* The plucked leaf is taken into the factory, spread on trays and left to wither in temperatures of 25–30

degrees centigrade. This process can take between 10–16 hours depending on the water content of the leaf. Today, in some factories the time is shortened with the help of warm-air fans.

2. *Orthodox and Unorthodox Manufacture.* The withered leaves are fed into machines which break them, thus releasing the enzymes or leaf juices, which on contact with air will oxidise, or ferment – as the process is known in the tea trade. The Orthodox method uses a machine which rolls the leaves. The Unorthodox method uses a CTC, Rotovane or Lawrie Tea Processor (LTP) machine to cut, tear and curl (CTC) or roll and cut the leaves.

3. *Fermentation.* The broken leaf is laid out on trays or placed in troughs in a cool and humid atmosphere for 3–4 hours, during which time it is gently turned at regular intervals, so that all the broken leaf comes into direct contact with the air and the juices oxidise. At the end of fermentation, the green broken leaf has turned a golden russet colour.

4. *Drying – or firing as it is often termed by the tea trade.* The fermented tea is fed on a conveyor belt slowly through a hot-air chamber, evaporating the leaf moisture. It emerges at the other end, dark brown in colour – in tea trade terms black – where it is collected for the next stage of "making".

5. *Sorting.* After drying the black tea is fed through a series of sieves, which sort or "grade" the tea into particle sizes. Factory tea-tasters taste the various grades of the "make", while the graded tea is packed into sacks or chests ready for its onward journey to auction centres, merchants and packers throughout the world.

OOLONG TEA – is a semi-fermented (or semi-oxidised) tea produced in China's Fujian province and in Taiwan. After withering (often in direct sunlight), the leaves are shaken in bamboo baskets to bruise the leaf edges. Then they are alternately shaken and spread out in the air until the veins and bruised edges turn a reddish colour while the rest of each leaf remains green. Sometimes the bruising process is carried out with the leaves wrapped inside cloth bags and rolled gently by hand or in a special machine. The oxidation period is stopped by firing the leaves at a higher temperature than for black teas. The leaf gives a pale, bright liquor with a very delicate flavour.

GREEN TEA – is an unfermented tea. The plucked leaf is withered and dried. The leaves are not broken so the juices are not able to escape and come into contact with oxygen in the air, therefore oxidisation or fermentation does not take place. Instead, the leaves are pan fried, baked or steamed to remove the enzymes that would cause deterioration of the tea. In China, they are then rolled or twisted, by hand or machine, to produce individual teas that each have their own characteristic appearance. For example, Gunpowder comes as tightly rolled grey-green pellets that look like lead shot; Chunmee looks like eyebrows; Lung Ching leaves are flat and green. In Japan, machines steam the leaves and then cut and roll them into flat, shiny dark green needles. Green teas give a pale, yellow-green liquor with a slightly pungent, herbal flavour that is best drunk without milk.

The finished product appears as small grey-green pellets or balls, which have a pale, bright greenish liquor with a delicate flavour.

TEA TRADING

Tea prices depend solely on quality, supply and demand and the majority of tea is sold at auction in producer countries. Selling brokers, acting for tea producers, auction teas to tea buyers, agents, merchants and brokers from around the world. Before attending an auction, be it Colombo in Sri Lanka; Limbe in Malawi; Mombasa – Kenya; Jakarta – Indonesia or the several auction centres in North and South India, everyone – sellers and buyers alike – will have tasted samples of the tea for auction. These will have been air-mailed to them by the producer or his broker. Some teas are also sold by private sale. In China, teas are sold within the various tea growing provinces.

GRADES OF TEA

Grade is the tea trade term used to describe the size of leaf particle. There are two main grades – pekoe and broken pekoe – pekoe, meaning leaf, is a corruption of the old Chinese word describing the down on the back of a white tea leaf or a very young tea leaf.

A pekoe grade (P) is, virtually, a whole leaf tea; broken pekoe (BP) describes the largest size leaf particles, so that a BOP – broken orange pekoe is a large leaf tea with plenty of young tea leaves in it. Pekoe fannings are the smaller particles, and these are divided into numerical classifications decreasing in particle size as the numbers increase – PF1, PF2, PF3 and PF4. Pekoe dust (PD) is the smallest leaf particle.

SPECIALITY TEAS

Speciality teas are teas that take their name from the area or country in which they are grown; a blend of teas for a particular time of day; a blend of teas named after a person; or a blend of teas to which fruit oils, flower petals or blossoms have been added, thus scenting the tea.

CHINA

Gunpowder

A green tea which, after it has been withered, is steamed and rolled into small pellets without breaking the veins in the tea leaves. These are then dried, and when brewed with boiling water, produce a very light, refreshing and pale-coloured tea. The name is said to have been given to the tea because the pellets look like gunshot or gunpowder of years gone by.

Jasmine

China tea which has been dried with Jasmine blossoms placed between the layers of tea. The tea therefore has a light, delicate aroma of Jasmine and a flavour to match.

Keemun

A black China tea, bright in colour with a round nutty flavour.

Lapsang Souchong

A large leaf tea distinguished by its smoky aroma and flavour. The story goes that when the Chinese first discovered tea, they used to dry it in the sun. Chinese legend claims that the smoking process was discovered by accident. At some point in China's history, an army camped in a tea factory that was full of drying leaves awaiting processing and so held up the normal working routine. When the soldiers left, the workers needed to prepare the leaves for the market as quickly as possible, so they lit open fires of pine wood to speed up the drying. The tea reached the market on time and a new flavour had been created. Today, the tea is still smoked but by more hygienic, modern methods.

Chunmee

A green tea from China. The leaves look like delicately curved eyebrows and give a golden yellow liquor with a light, smooth, slightly plummy taste.

Tekuanyin

A very high quality oolong tea from Fujian Province. The name means 'Tea of the Iron Goddess of Mercy' and the dark, crinkly leaves give a subtly, fragrant infusion that is best drunk without milk.

Rose Congou

A large-leafed black tea scented with rose petals. The manufacture of 'gongfu' teas demands great skill in the handling of the leaves, the temperature control and the timing of each part of the process.

Yunnan

A black tea from the province of Yunnan in the south west of China. It has a rich malty flavour similar to that of Assam teas and is best drunk with a little milk. It makes an excellent breakfast tea.

FORMOSA OOLONG

Tea production started in Formosa (not Taiwan) in the 1850s when farmers from China's Fujian Province emigrated to the island and established plantations there. Production methods are the same as those used on the Chinese mainland and the best oolongs are grown high up on the slopes of Mount Dung Ding.

JAPAN
Sencha

The most commonly drunk green tea in Japan. The dark green flat needles give a pale yellow infusion that has a light delicate flavour.

INDIA
Assam

A blend of tea grown in Assam in North India. It is a full-bodied tea with a dark liquor and a rich malty flavour which is ideal as the first cup of tea in the morning. It really wakes you up. Such teas are used in everyday popular blends because of the full-bodied richness.

Darjeeling

Known as the 'Champagne of Teas', Darjeeling is grown several thousands of feet above sea level in the foothills of the Himalayan mountains. Darjeeling teas have a very light delicate flavour.

Nilgiri

The tea from the Nilgiri Hills in Southern India is light, bright and delicate in taste.

SRI LANKA (CEYLON)

Ceylon Blend

Ceylon teas span the entire spectrum of tea production, from low to high grown teas. By blending teas from different areas of the island, Sri Lanka is able to offer a very wide choice of flavour and characteristics. Some blends are full-bodied, others are light and delicate, but all are brisk, full-flavoured and have a bright colour.

Dimbula

Grown 5,000 ft above sea level in Sri Lanka, Dimbula teas are light and bright in colour with a crisp, strong flavour which leaves the mouth feeling fresh and clean. Dimbula was one of the first areas of Sri Lanka to be planted with tea after the demise of the coffee estates in 1870.

Uva

A fine flavoured tea from the eastern slopes of the Central Mountains of Sri Lanka. Uva tea is bright in colour, has a dry crisp taste and makes an ideal mid-morning or after lunch tea.

KENYA

Tea from Kenya is very bright and colourful which makes it easily distinguishable. It has a reddish, coppery tint with a pleasant, brisk flavour. Kenya tea is widely used in tea bag blends and is an ideal drink at any time of the day or night.

SOUTH AFRICA

Zulu Tea

A black CTC tea from KwaZulu – the only South African tea to be exported for international consumption. The flavour is lively and strong and is best drunk with milk.

INDONESIA

Indonesian teas are light and flavoursome. Most are sold for blending purposes as this produces good financial rewards in terms of foreign currency for the country. It is also possible to buy Indonesian tea as a speciality tea. It is extremely refreshing taken without milk, garnished with a slice of lemon, making it an ideal drink for the figure conscious.

SPECIALITY TEA BLENDS

English Breakfast

Traditionally a blend of Assam and Ceylon teas that gives pungency and flavour to help digest a full English breakfast and give a good brisk start to the day. Today, many English Breakfast blends also include an East African tea from Malawi, Tanzania, Zimbabwe or Kenya which gives the blend a coppery brightness.

Afternoon Tea

Traditionally, a blend of delicate Darjeeling tea and high-grown Ceylon tea to produce a refreshing but light tea which makes an ideal companion to cucumber sandwiches, cream pastries and fruit cakes.

Earl Grey

Traditionally, a blend of black China teas treated with the natural oils of the citrus bergamot fruit which gives the blend its perfumed aroma and flavour. Earl Grey tea is said to have originally been blended for the second Earl Grey by a mandarin after Britain had completed a successful diplomatic mission to China.

House Blend

Some menus offer 'a pot of tea', others 'a pot of house blend tea'. This tea is equivalent to – if not better than – the type of tea the majority of us buy to use at home.

In tea trade language, it is known as a 'popular brand leading blend'. In catering terms, it will be a Quality Award tea, as identified by The Tea Council's Catering Tea Quality Programme. No matter whether it is loose leaf or in a tea bag, a house blend tea is a work of art. It can contain 15–35 different teas which are blended in order to achieve the consistent quality, flavour and characteristics consumers expect from their favourite 'popular brand leading blend'. Some of the teas are seasonal, some are not. During the year or plucking season, adverse weather conditions can affect the quality of any of the teas, in which case the blender has to find other teas that will produce the same flavour and characteristics and ensure the consistency and quality of the blend. To do this, a taster/blender will taste between 200 and 1,000 teas a day and will adjust the 'recipe' so that we can enjoy our favourite cup of tea all day, and everyday.

FLAVOURED TEAS

Flavoured teas are real tea (*Camellia Sinensis*) blended with fruit, spices or herbs. For example, fruit flavoured teas such as apple, lemon, orange, mango or blackcurrant consist of tea blended with pieces of fruit peel or blossom or treated with the natural fruit juice or oil (known as the zest). Spiced tea, such as cinnamon or nutmeg, is tea blended with a particular spice, and herb flavoured teas have the dried herb added to the blend, as in the case of mint or sage tea.

In all cases, the fruit, spice or herb flavours the real tea and should not be confused with herbal or fruit infusions, which contain no tea.

TISANES AND FRUIT INFUSIONS

Tisane, according to Roget's Thesaurus, is a soft drink or a tonic. Stemming from the French, the term is used to describe infusions of mainly herbal leaves such as camomile, peppermint, nettle, etc and does not contain real tea. Fruit infusions – today known as fruit teas – like herbal infusions, do not contain one leaf of real tea. The zest, dried pieces of peel or fruit blossoms, are blended with dried hibiscus leaves to produce a refreshing fruit flavoured infusion.

HOW TO CHOOSE A GOOD TEA AND STORE IT

When a tea taster, whether a producer, buyer or seller, looks at a tea, there are certain things that he or she can tell by just looking.

For example, the tea must appear 'even'. This means that the dry leaf sample the taster examines is all of the same leaf particle size. Not only does it give the dry leaf a pleasing appearance, but it does mean that when brewed, the flavour and pungency are all released from the leaf simultaneously. An uneven blend – leaf of varying particle sizes – means that when brewing, the flavour and pungency are released according to the varying sizes of leaf particle, giving an unbalanced overall flavour and quality.

Keep your tea in an airtight caddy in a cool dry storage area, away from other strong smelling foods as tea absorbs other flavours very easily.

THE ART OF TEA TASTING

Tea tasters train for five years and most of them will tell you that they go on learning the art for the rest of their lives. Tea brokers and buyers taste samples of the teas which are to be sold at auction and price them accordingly. Tasters check the colour of the dry leaf, smell the wet leaf and tea liquor, then sip and slurp the liquor itself. In all cases, they are looking for quality and flavour. They also make comparisons with tea from the same estates. Tasters working with specific companies are also looking for the qualities and flavours which will keep your favourite blend consistent day in day out, year after year.

Experiment with different teas to find your favourite, or you might like to blend your own. A few leaves of Lapsang Souchong or Earl Grey added to your everyday tea will give it a completely new flavour.

Tea tasters use a wide vocabulary to describe the appearance and flavour of tea. The following are the terms used most frequently to describe the dry leaf:

Black: a black appearance is desirable, preferably with "bloom".

Bloom: a sign of good manufacture and sorting, a sheen that has not been lost through over-handling or over-sorting.

Even: teas true to their grade, consisting of pieces of leaf of fairly even size.

Make: a term used to describe a tea manufacture batch.

The following are the terms used most frequently to describe the infused tea leaf:

Bright: a lively bright appearance, which usually indicates that the tea will produce a bright liquor.

Dull: lacks brightness and usually denotes poor tea. Can be due to faulty making (manufacture) and firing, or a high moisture content.

Green: when referring to black tea it means the leaf has been underfermented, or alternatively it can be a leaf plucked from immature bushes and will often when liquored result in a raw or light liquor. Can also be caused by poor rolling during making or manufacture.

The following are the terms used most frequently for the taste of the tea liquor:

Baggy: an unpleasant taste, resulting from tea being carried or wrapped in unlined hessian bags.

Bakey: an over-fired tea which means too much moisture has been taken from the leaf while drying.

Bitter: an unpleasant taste associated with raw teas.

Body: a liquor having both fullness and strength.

Bright: denotes a lively fresh tea with good keeping quality.

Brisk: the most 'live' characteristic, results from good manufacture.

Coloury: indicates useful depth of colour and strength.

Earthy: caused by damp storage of tea but can also describe a taste that is sometimes 'climatically inherent' in teas from certain regions.

Empty: a liquor lacking fullness; with no substance.

Fruity: can be due to over-fermenting during manufacture and/or bacterial infection before firing or drying. Unlike wine, this is not a desirable taste.

Hard: a very pungent liquor; a desirable quality in tea.

Malty: a desirable character in some Assam teas. A full, bright tea with a malty taste.

Mature: not bitter or flat.

Plain: a liquor that is clean but lacking in desirable characteristics.

Point: a bright, acidic and penetrating characteristic.

Rasping: a very course and harsh liquor.

Thick: liquor with good colour and strength.

If you would like to learn more tea vocabulary, please look up the Glossary on our website: http://www.teacouncil.co.uk

TEA PAIRINGS

Despite being our national drink, there is just one time in the day when tea gives way to a competitive drink, coffee, after dinner. Coffee is usually taken in preference to tea despite the fact that tea, unlike coffee, is a *digestif* which calms and soothes a full stomach and cleans the palate – of key importance when a final glass of wine or liqueur is being enjoyed after the meal.

In addition, teas can be paired with specific foods and wines in order to enhance both the food and the wine whilst highlighting the specific qualities of the teas themselves.

Working with The Academy of Food and Wine, The Tea Council has identi-fied specific pairings to demonstrate these exciting possibilities. Pairings can be created to partner special desserts, cheeses, foods and liqueurs. Pairings may also be a special feature of afternoon tea.

The Tea Council commissioned research which revealed that 53% of the restaurants in the UK fail to offer tea on their menus and only 22% of customers request tea when it is not featured. This suggests that the hotel and restaurant trade is losing revenue of £260 million by not offering tea.

The matrix illustrates tea's potential as an ideal after-dinner or after-lunch drink, as well as offering ample choice for a delicious afternoon tea.

TRY SOME OF THESE DELICIOUS TEA PAIRINGS

TEA	SANDWICHES	AFTERNOON TEA PASTRIES/DESSERTS	CHEESE	WINE	LIQUEUR
Ceylon	Cucumber or Tomato Sandwich	Tarte Au Citron	Mature Cheddar	Fine dessert wine	Chartreuse yellow/green
Kenya	Beef and Horseradish or Ham Sandwich	Chocolate Cake (rich)	Austrian Smoked	New World Cabernet Sauvignon	Drambuie
Darjeeling	Cream Cheese or Egg and Cress Sandwich	Cream Desserts	Cream Cheese	Zinfandel type wines Shiraz *or* Syrah	Armagnac
Lapsang	Chicken or Smoked Salmon Sandwich	Walnut Cake	Stilton	New World Chardonnay	Tawny Port
Earl Grey	Fine Pâté or Ham and Mustard Sandwich	Crème Brûlée	Leicester	Valpolicella *or* Beaujolais	

COOKING WITH TEA

In China, tea has been used in cooking for many years – as an ingredient added to sesame seeds, popped corn and soy seeds to make little rice flour cakes, and as a vegetable boiled and mixed with spices and eaten as a snack. Marbled eggs are traditionally stained with a tea infusion and poultry is often smoked over the leaves. In Japan, green tea leaves are added to the water used to boil noodles or rice, are sometimes eaten with a few drops of soy sauce, and green tea flavoured ice creams, sweets and biscuits are becoming very popular. In Britain, the idea of cooking with tea is by no means a new one. In the eighteenth century, a tea infusion was used to flavour tea creams and custards, and later, in Victorian days, tea cream ices were sometimes included in recipe books. Chefs today are beginning to use tea again as an everyday ingredient and, as we now know that tea is so good for us, it is an ideal time to experiment at home. Use freshly brewed good quality tea and be careful not to make the infusion so strong that it overwhelms the flavour of the food. When adding to marinades and poaching liquids,

etc., use a light tea such as oolong, jasmine or Earl Grey, but for soaking raisins, sultanas, currants and other dried fruits for fruit cakes and desserts, the rich malty flavour of an Assam or a breakfast tea will not be too powerful.

Try some of the following ideas:

● flavour salad dressings with a teaspoonful of a green tea infusion that has been boiled to reduce it to a concentrated liquid

● smoke chicken or duck in a closed wok over a mixture of tea, rice, brown sugar, cinnamon and orange zest

● add a little cold tea to batters used for frying fish

● marinade kippers in a light infusion of China oolong before grilling

● add a little Earl Grey or Lapsang Souchong to the water in which you boil ham

● add a little tea infusion to your usual marinade for spare ribs or chops before grilling or barbecuing

● when steaming fish, add a little tea infusion with stock and herbs to the bottom of the pan

● poach duck in the oven in a mixture of Earl Grey infusion, honey and lemon or orange juice

● flavour sorbets and ices creams with a light infusion of Earl Grey, green tea or fruit or flower flavoured tea

● add jasmine tea or Earl Grey to the syrup used for a fresh fruit salad

● soak dried fruit in an infusion of tea before adding to cakes and puddings

● add a small pinch of green tea leaves (jasmine or sencha) to the water in which you boil pasta or rice

TEA COCKTAILS

Tea makes an excellent base for all sorts of hot and chilled punches and cocktails.

Here are a few ideas:

● mix an infusion of Keemun with sparkling apple juice, fresh lemon juice, a little sugar or honey to taste, and plenty of ice

● dilute an infusion of vanilla flavoured sencha with honey and fresh lime juice, a little sparkling mineral water and a few ice cubes

● add lime cordial, sparkling mineral water and a few bruised mint leaves to an infusion of Ceylon tea and serve very cold

● mix sparkling white wine with an iced tea infusion, sweeten with honey or sugar and serve over ice

● add one or two cinnamon sticks and a few cloves to the pot when brewing black tea, then mix the infusion with warm cider, orange slices and sugar or honey to taste

● add one or two teaspoons of whisky or rum to hot tea and sweeten to taste

● to make Indian style 'chai', boil together 2 teabags in milk with sugar to taste, a little ground ginger, 2–3 a cinnamon sticks, a few whole cloves, 8–10 cardamom pods and a whole nutmeg. Simmer and then strain into a mug or cup.

THE BEAUTY OF TEA

Over the years, beauty advice and health tips have included such suggestions as placing cold used tea bags or pads of cotton wool soaked in cold tea on tired eyes as a refreshing compress, bathing sunburned skin with cold tea to help reduce the irritation and redness and speed the healing process, soaking tired and aching feet in a warm tea solution, rinsing hair with tea to bring out the shine and add richness to the colour, and using tea as a cleansing tonic for oily skin. Recently, a number of new skin care products that include tea amongst their ingredients have appeared on the market.

The components of tea that have begun to interest the cosmetics industry are the anti-oxidant flavonoids which can help our skin and other body cells to fight the 'free radicals' that cause premature ageing and can lead to the development of such illnesses as cancer. Green tea is one of the most commonly used flavonoids in skin care products, and,

over the past two or three years, a wide range of products has become generally available, including sun blocks, anti-ageing creams, moisturisers, skin gels, face masks, bath powders, facial toners, shampoos, conditioners, and body contouring products. Anti-cellulite treatments also often contain tea and some women claim that they have no cellulite on their thighs because they used tea to stain their legs during the war when nylon and silk stockings were not easily obtainable.

Perfumiers too have been using tea in their designer scents – not because of its health benefits but because it adds a refreshing and delicate aroma. Calvin Klein's scent CK One, has a 'green tea accord' which "travels from top to bottom, contributing to the signature of the CK One fragrance". And Bulgari's Eau Parfumee "is born from the culture of tea and the more profound sense of the rituals tied to it, combining the finest aromas of tea with distinctly Mediterranean fragrances".

So today, as well as drinking tea, we have the added option of wearing it and bathing in it. It is a truly flexible and adaptable herb.

TEA AND HEALTH

HEALTH AND DIET

W.E. Gladstone, Prime Minister of Britain in the second half of Queen Victoria's reign, drank tea morning, noon and night. He said "if you are cold, tea will warm you but if you are heated, it will cool you. If you are depressed, it will cheer you up but if you are excited, it will calm you".

In Britain we each consume on average three and a half cups of tea daily – a staggering 185 million cups of tea are consumed in Britain each day.

YOUR DAILY CUPPA

Tea is a natural drink and taken on its own, tea has no calories. However 98% of the population take it with milk and three and a half cups of tea a day may provide you with significant amounts of the following recommended nutrient intake: 16% calcium, 10% zinc, 10% folic acid, riboflavin (B2) and vitamins B1 and B6. Tea is also a good source of manganese which is essential for bone growth and the body's development and potassium which is vital for maintaining a normal heart beat.

TEA AND FLUID REPLACEMENT

Approximately 50-70% of our body weight is made up of water. Around two thirds of it is held within the cells, while the other third travels around the body in the form of blood and other fluids. Therefore it is recommended that we drink at least 1.5 litres of fluid a day to prevent dehydration and ensure that we pass enough urine to keep us healthy. Tea is a good way to take our fluids since, when taken with milk, it contains the minerals and nutrients needed in our diet to maintain optimum health.

TEA AND ANTIOXIDANTS

Tea contains a group of compounds classified as polyphenols; these generate antioxidant activity. Antioxidant activity helps to defend the body from, and repair the damage caused by free radicals. Free radicals are highly reactive molecules which have been implicated in the slow chain reaction of damage leading to heart disease and cancer.

TEA AND CARDIOVASCULAR DISEASE PREVENTION

Antioxidant activity may also help combat the risk of developing heart disease. Studies provide evidence that polyphenols can have a beneficial effect on two long established heart disease factors: high blood pressure and high blood cholesterol.

TEA AND CANCER PREVENTION

Studies provide evidence that polyphenols can offer protection from and a beneficial effect against certain cancers.

TEA AND ORAL HEALTH

A regular intake of fluoride is recommended to protect against dental caries and gum disease. Tea is a natural source of fluoride and just one cup can contain 0.3 to 0.5mg. Studies show that the polyphenolic activity of tea may also benefit oral health.

For more information, please visit www.teahealth.co.uk.

THE TEA COUNCIL

The Tea Council is an independent, non-profit making organisation funded by the UK tea trade and the governments of seven tea producing countries. Its aim is to promote tea generically in the United Kingdom.

Its main activities are:

■ The promotion of tea as a natural and healthy beverage.

■ Researching the role of tea in a healthy lifestyle.

■ Internet websites:

www.teacouncil.co.uk

www.teahealth.co.uk

www.tea.co.uk

www.teatrail.co.uk

■ Education resources for primary, secondary and further education.

■ The Catering Tea Quality Programme which monitors the quality of catering tea and assures its quality standards, whilst providing a database through which caterers can check the quality of the tea they are using.

■ The creation and administration of The Guild of Tea Shops.

■ The Tea Council runs various awards throughout the year to highlight and promote the importance of making, serving and selling good quality tea.

■ Tea Pairings.

For more information, please write to:

The Tea Council Limited

No. 9, The Courtyard

Gowan Avenue

London

SW6 6RH

Tel: 020 7371 7787

Fax: 020 7371 7958

http:\\www.teacouncil.co.uk

email: tea@teacouncil.co.uk

S O U T H   W E S T
R E G I O N A L   M A P

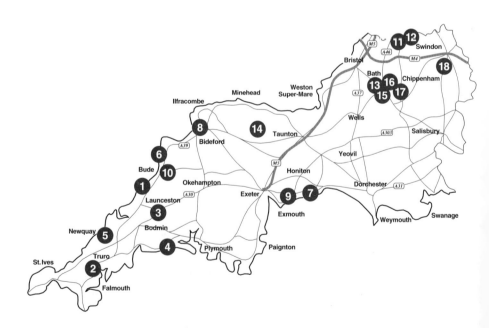

CARPENTER'S KITCHEN

Owners: Debbie and Geoff Beszant

**The Harbour, Boscastle
Cornwall PL35 0HD
Tel: 01840 250595**

Directions
Take the B3266 from Camelford or the B3263 from Tintagel. Follow signs to Boscastle Harbour.

Opening times
Open April–October, daily 10.30–5.30 pm. March and November, weekends only, 10.30 am–5 pm. Christmas, 27th December–1st January inclusive 10.30 am–5 pm.Now available, small amount of seating outside.

Awards
1996 & 98 Tea Council Award of Excellence

Local Interest:
Walk around this fascinating typically Cornish village with its narrow lanes and old cottages. Also explore the site of Bottreaux Castle and 60 acres of the surrounding National Trust cliffs and land with walks in all directions and fantastic views.

The site of Carpenter's Kitchen was used as a carpenter's workshop for almost one hundred years. When the last owner, Arthur Olde, retired in 1987, his daughter, Debbie, and son-in-law, Geoff, recognised the potential of the site, hence the now thriving tearoom. From the front door there is a view over the river and harbour, and a small amount of seating is available on the forecourt. Inside, Geoff and Debbie have kept the rustic country style with polished wooden furniture, a traditional dado rail, wooden floor and wisteria stencilled walls that are hung with old photographs and paintings of old Boscastle and carpenters who previously worked here.

The menu is designed to incorporate all the home cooking that makes Carpenter's Kitchen so popular with local people and visitors. There is a daily selection of goodies in the cold cabinet, and the sweet trolley usually holds some real favourites such as meringues, cheesecake and fruit pies. And if you can't be tempted by the cakes, clotted cream can be dolloped on freshly baked scones or Cornish splits. Seasonal treats include fresh Port Isaac crab in the summer, and freshly prepared soups for chilly spring and autumn days. *Teas served:* House Blend (a blend of Indian and Kenya teas), Earl Grey, Darjeeling, Assam, Lapsang Souchong, Lemon. *Fruit flavoured teas and herbal infusions are also available.*

CHARLOTTE'S TEA-HOUSE

Owners: Tony and Cynthia Martin

**Coinage Hall
No 1 Boscawen Street
Truro, Cornwall TR1 2QU
Tel: 01872 261133**

Directions
The Coinage Hall is in the centre of Truro, opposite the Hall for Cornwall, directly behind the bronze War Memorial. Charlotte's is on the 1st floor.

Opening times
Open all year.
Monday–Saturday, 10 am–5 pm.
Sunday, closed.

Local Interest:
Truro is the administrative centre of the Duchy of Cornwall, home to the County Museum, and central to all the county's resorts and places of historical interest. The fine 19th century cathedral dominates the excellent shopping centre.

The Coinage Hall in Truro has a history that goes back to 1302 and the halcyon days of Cornish tin mining, but the present Grade II listed building was built in 1848 and has recently been lovingly restored by Tony and Cynthia. Charlotte's Tea-House, on the 1st floor of the building, is the realisation of their dream of creating a sanctuary of Victorian tranquillity just a few steps from the city's busy streets. The ambience is enhanced by crystal chandeliers and period furniture, home made cakes served on silver-plated cake stands, and waitresses in period costume.

The emphasis is on quality, and every care is taken to provide the best. Charlotte's was voted the top tea house in Cornwall in the Annual West Country Cooking Guide to Eating Out 2000/2001. Everything on the menu is made on the premises and there is always a tempting display of cakes. Light lunches include potato toasties, omelettes and salads, and there are cream teas and Charlotte's speciality high teas – all made to order. Visitors can browse in the antique and collectors showrooms, or visit the wonderful selection of Italian drapes on the same floor as the tearoom. *Teas served:* House Blend, Assam, Ceylon, China Yunnan, Darjeeling, Earl Grey, Lady Grey, Jasmine, Lapsang Souchong. *Fruit flavoured teas and herbal infusions are also available.*

MAD HATTER'S

Owner: Vicki James-Allen

28 Church Street
Launceston, Cornwall
PL15 8AR
Tel: 01566 777188

Directions

Launceston is just off the A30 in North Cornwall. Mad Hatter's is in the centre of the town, 30 yards from the town square, opposite WH Smiths.

Opening times

Open summer, 9.30 am–5.30 pm except Sunday, 11 am–4.30 pm.
Winter, 10.30 am–5 pm every day except Wednesday, 10.30 am–2 pm and closed Sunday. Opening times vary: please telephone to confirm.

Local Interest:

Launceston is the ancient capital of Cornwall and there is a castle run by English Heritage, a museum and a Town Trail which walks you past all the interesting landmarks of the town.

Vicki James-Allen doesn't believe that quality and high standards have to be at the expense of entertainment, and admits that being "as Mad as a Hatter" helped in creating this very idiosyncratic tearoom where Lewis Carroll's characters are everywhere. On Saturdays and holidays, she is even to be seen serving tea dressed as her alter ego in top hat and tails. Vicki designed and decorated the shop herself and created the wonderfully humorous menu that offers Mad Hatter's Platters of cheese, tuna or smoked ham with bread and pickles, Alice's Scrumptious Sandwiches, March Hare's Marvellous Cakes and Mad Hatter's Specials. A new range of very popular toasted sandwiches includes a Mouldy Old

Dough (stilton and mushroom) and even Call the Paramedics! (raspberry jam, chocolate chips and bananas served with clotted cream). But the favourite item has to be the Indecisive Cake Taster whereby those tempted by several of the home made, calorie-laden gateaux can sample any three or, in desperation, ask the waitress to choose for them. Also featured – a special Dormouse selection of delicious food lower in saturated fat and sugar and higher in fibre, and foods suitable for diabetics. *Teas served:* Assam, Ceylon, China, Darjeeling, Earl Grey, English Breakfast, Jasmine, Kenya, Lapsang Souchong, Mad Hatter's Special Blend (lightly spiced). *Scented teas and herbal infusions are also available.*

THE PLANTATION CAFE

Owners: Ann and Maurice Vaughan

**The Coombes, Polperro
Cornwall PL13 2RG
Tel: 01503 272223**

Directions

Park in the main car park and walk to the Plantation Cafe which is on the right hand side of the main road, half way between the car park and the harbour.

Opening times

Open Easter–end of October.
Monday–Friday, 10.30 am–5.30 pm
(9 pm in peak season).
Saturday, closed.
Sunday, 10.30 am–5.30 pm.

Local Interest:

Polperro is a traditional fishing village once well known for its smuggling. Visit the new Teglio Museum that tells the history of Polperro and South East Cornwall and take a pleasure trip in a fishing boat to see the coves and the caves along the coast. Also look out for the stories about Piskeys, the Cornish fairy folk, and their Queen, Joan the Wad, and King Sam Spriggin.

In the vigorous days of Victorian expansion and enterprise, a local Polperro man went off adventuring in North America and made a fortune on the plantations there. He later returned to the place where he was born and used some of the money to build this black and white house right beside the River Pol – hence the name of the tearoom. The building stands in a conservation area so its solid, secure Victorian exterior of traditional Cornish stone and Delabole slate roof will never change. Inside, the Victorian theme is continued with exposed black and white beams, an open fireplace with its copper hood, oak tables, wheelback chairs, copper and brass pots and pans and collections of teapots and Delft ware to decorate the walls.

The river runs peacefully alongside the lovingly-tended garden that has won awards for its beauty and colour and provides a stunning setting for lunch or tea. The menu offers all sorts of local specialities – Cornish pasties, cheese and onion pies, sandwiches made with locally caught crab, and delicious home made cakes, scones and fruit pies served with Cornish clotted cream. Real traditional Cornish treats! *Teas served:* House Blend, Earl Grey, Assam, Darjeeling, Lapsang Souchong, Ceylon. *Fruit flavoured teas and herbal infusions are also offered.*

TRENANCE COTTAGE TEA ROOM & GARDENS

Proprietors: Bob and Judy Poole

Trenance Cottage, Trenance Lane
Newquay, Cornwall TR7 2HX
Tel/Fax: 01637 872034

Directions
From the town centre, proceed down Edgcumbe Avenue past Waterworld/zoo, under the viaduct, past Trenance Gardens and Heritage

Cottages into Trevemper Road with Rose Gardens and Boating Lakes on the right. Trenance Cottage lies directly opposite the lakes. An Edwardian bus service and Shuttle train stop opposite during the season.

Opening times
Open all year for accommodation. Tea Room open from March–November, 10.30 am–5.00 pm, every day of the week. In winter, times vary so please telephone.

Local Interest:
Trenance Cottage overlooks the beautiful Trenance Gardens where you can walk, take a trip on the boating lake or visit Heritage Cottages – Victorian houses set out as they would have been in the 19th century and including an arts and crafts shop. Also close to the zoo and leisure centre.

A visit to Trenance Cottage means taking a step back in time through a wonderful Wisteria arch at the entrance to the Georgian villa where Judy and Bob Poole have recreated the tearoom that existed here well before the second world war. The building was virtually derelict when the couple bought it in 1986 but they have chopped away the tree roots that were growing from unlikely parts of the house, repaired the roof, and generally renovated and restored it to its earlier charm. Like so many people, they had grown tired of plastic cups, tea bags and poor quality food and decided to go into business themselves in order to offer something rather better. The tearoom seats up to 30 visitors while the terraced gardens can accommodate 80 visitors. Serving morning coffee, light lunches, homemade cakes and scones, the menu features a variety of Cornish produce – crab, cheeses, pasties, smoked mackerel, saffron buns, freshly made ice cream, spring water and, of course, clotted cream. Many of the local products are offered for sale and make ideal presents. For those wishing to stay, there are three letting bedrooms offering a high standard of accommodation. *Teas served:* Tearoom Blend, Assam, Darjeeling, Earl Grey, English Breakfast, Lapsang Souchong, China Green, decaffeinated, other speciality teas. *Herbal infusions are also offered.*

THE OLD RECTORY FARM TEAROOMS

Owners: R. B. Savage & V. K. Metters

Rectory Farm, Morwenstow
Near Bude, Cornwall EX23 9SR
Tel: 01288 331251

Directions
From the A39, from Bideford to Bude, turn off at the sign to Morwenstow. Follow signs to the village and church. The tearoom is next to the church.

Opening times
Open Easter–end of October.
Monday–Thursday and Sunday, 11 am–6 pm.
Friday and Saturday, 11 am–6 pm and 7.30 pm–9.30 pm.

Local Interest:
Only ten minutes away is some of the most spectacular scenery in North Cornwall. Next door is the ancient Church of St John the Baptist and famous graveyard with the graves of shipwrecked sailors.

Rectory Farm has a long long history and is mentioned in a document dated 1296 when it belonged to the monks of St John of Bridgwater. The main hall of the house with its heavy oak beams and ancient stone flagged floor is now the tearoom and restaurant and has been run by the same family for nearly 50 years. It was the current owner who set it up when she realised that a lot of people were passing her door on their walks along the coastal footpath that runs right past the front door. She recognised the potential for a busy tearoom and created a warm, traditional interior with Victorian furniture and chintz curtains and today, there is a steady stream of customers right through the summer season. As well as enjoying high quality lunches, teas and dinners, you can buy local jams, chutneys and other produce from the little shop area.

Visitors come from all over the world to see the church of St John the Baptist, made famous by Parson Hawker, an eccentric who introduced Harvest Festival to British churches and wrote the famous Cornish anthem, 'Trelawney'. Rectory Farm, which is next door, gives them a chance to also enjoy a really good traditional English tea. *Teas served:* India, Earl Grey, Lapsang Souchong, Gunpowder, Keemun, Assam, Jasmine. *Herbal infusions are also offered.*

THE CLOCK TOWER TEAROOMS

Owners: Stewart and June Fraser

**Connaught Gardens
Peak Hill Road, Sidmouth
Devon EX10 8RZ
Tel: 01395 512477**

Directions
From the town centre, proceed to the sea front and turn right. Take the road up a slight incline following signs to Manor Road car park. Connaught Gardens is directly opposite the car park and the tearooms are in the clock tower, at the top of Jacobs Ladder.

Opening times
Open all year except Christmas Day.
Monday–Sunday inclusive, 10 am–5 pm.
Longer hours in summer.

Local Interest:
Sidmouth has two beaches that are good for bathing, sailing and fishing, and the town has good shops, and holiday accommodation. The surrounding countryside offers wonderful walks over the cliffs and headlands.

Previously in a state of ruin, The Clock Tower has been lovingly restored by the Frasers and now offers an unusual and charming venue for lunch or tea. It stands on the remains of ancient lime kilns and once served as a boat-house, but today, the castellated building, with its gothic-style windows, has been brought back to life. The old stone walls cascade with plants and flowers and visitors who choose a table outside in the beautiful gardens can relish the amazing views of the sea and the stunning coastline. Inside, there are low beams decorated with amazing wood carvings by a local artist, and the polished wooden floors and warm tones of the wooden furniture create a relaxed, friendly, welcoming atmosphere.

The selection of hot and cold drinks (including Ovaltine and hot chocolate) and the range of sandwiches and toasties, jacket potatoes, pizzas, ploughmans, full lunches and tea time traditionals makes this a good place in both the cold of winter and the blazing heat of summer. There are scones with clotted cream and jam, toasted teacakes and a selection of cakes and gateaux for those with a sweet tooth. *Teas served:* House Blend, Assam, Darjeeling, Earl Grey.

THE COMMODORE HOTEL

Owner: Bruce Woolaway

Marine Parade
Instow, North Devon
EX39 4JN
Tel: 01271 860347
Fax: 01271 861233

Directions
From the M5 take Exit 27 for the North
Devon Link Road. Take the turning to Instow

signposted just before Torridge Bridge. Follow
signs for Instow seafront and these will bring
you to Marine Parade.

Opening times
Open to non-residents all year, 7.30 am–9.30 pm.
Afternoon tea is served from 3–6 pm.

Awards
1997 Top Tea Place of The Year

Local Interest:
*The historic towns of Bideford and Barnstaple are nearby
and Instow is within easy reach of Exmoor and Dartmoor
National Parks.*

Originally a Georgian gentleman's residence, this waterside hotel sits elegantly overlooking the mouth of the rivers Taw and Torridge in one of North Devon's prettiest locations. The Woolaways, a local Devon family, have owned the hotel since 1969 and they have created a stylish, welcoming environment where views of the palm trees, sweeping lawns that slope gently down to the sandy shore and the constantly changing waterfront scenery make it a perfect place for afternoon tea. In summer months, relax on the terrace and watch the yachts scudding by with billowing sails, and in the chillier winter months, take shelter from the sea breezes in the comfortable lounge.

The hotel's marine setting is echoed in the menu where a good range of seafoods is offered for lunchtime savouries and in open sandwiches. And, since this is the home of clotted cream, don't miss the cream tea, or, for a change, try a clotted cream ice cream or treat yourself to one of the rich desserts or cakes that are served with generous portions of either the clotted or double variety of the delicious indulgence. *Teas served:* Assam, Darjeeling, Lapsang Souchong, Earl Grey, Traditional PG Tips. *Flavoured teas and herbal infusions are also offered.*

THE COSY TEAPOT

Owners: Pat and Norman Palmer

13 Fore Street, Budleigh Salterton
Devon EX9 6NH
Tel: 01395 444016

Directions
Budleigh Salterton is 11 miles from Junction 30
of the M5 and 4 miles east of Exmouth. The
Cosy Teapot is situated at the lower end of the
main street, towards the seafront.

Opening times
Open all year except Tuesday and
Wednesday. Monday, Thursday,
Friday, Saturday, Sunday,
10 am–5 pm in summer,
10 am–4.30 pm in winter.

Local Interest:
Sir Walter Raleigh's birth place is a couple of miles away
and Milais' famous painting of Sir Walter on the sea wall
is about 50 yards from the shop. The local museum
specialises in old lace and there are cliff walks and
wonderful surrounding countryside.

This delightful Victorian style tea room is housed in what was once – in about 1880 – the 'Library', and later a shoe-mender's shop. To reach the shop, you have to cross a small bridge that straddles the little stream running right past the door. Once inside, visitors from all over the world enjoy the restful pink, white and burgundy colour scheme, fine Royal Albert china, and a menu that offers sandwiches, toasted sandwiches, soups and salads throughout the day, and a superior range of home made cakes made locally by talented cooks. At tea time, there is a Devonshire Cream tea, or as a variation on the traditional theme, the Cosy Teacake

Special with a toasted teacake, strawberry jam and clotted cream. And for those who really wish to indulge, the Banana Toastie is a toasted banana sandwich drenched with sugar, topped with caramel sauce and served with clotted cream or ice cream. Popular cakes and desserts include almond and cherry, coffee and walnut, sticky ginger pudding. The tea shop also sells a range of teas, farm made jams and sauces, books, tea towels and other tea-related items. *Teas served:* Assam, Darjeeling, Earl Grey, Lady Grey, English Breakfast, Lapsang Souchong, Traditional English Afternoon. *Herbal infusions are also offered.*

COURT BARN COUNTRY HOUSE HOTEL

Owners: Susan and Robert Wood

Clawton, Holsworthy
Devon EX22 6PS
Tel: 01409 271219 Fax: 01409 271309

Directions
Clawton is 2½ miles south of Holsworthy off the A388 (from Bude to Launceston). Court Barn is next to Clawton's 12th century church.

Opening times
Open all year except the first week of January.
Monday–Sunday, 10 am–5.30 pm.
Bookings preferred for lunch.

Awards
1987 & 89 Tea Council Award of Excellence
Egon Ronay recommended
AA Rosette

Local Interest:
Clawford Vineyard, several local nature trails, Cookworthy Woods, sailing on Roadford and Tomao Lakes, Holsworthy Pannier Market (Wednesday). A short drive to Bude and National Trust beaches and coastal walks.

Court Barn is a charming Victorian House, rebuilt in 1853 from a 16th century manor house known as Court Baron. The hotel stands in five acres of beautiful tranquil formal gardens hidden amongst rolling Devon countryside and close to the spectacular National Trust and English Heritage coastline.

The house is filled with antiques, paintings and decorative objects. Fresh flowers fill the elegant dining rooms and lounges and there is a crackling log fire in the cosy bar, creating a warm, friendly and relaxed atmosphere. And on balmy summer days, the garden makes an idyllic setting for a special Devon clotted cream tea with one of the 45 teas on the menu. For the more energetic, there is croquet, lawn tennis and badminton or gentle strolls around the garden.

The menu is crammed with wonderful home baked sweets and savouries, soups and pâtés, vegetarian dishes, sandwiches and cakes such as Marsala and Almond, Honey and Cherry, Chocolate and Walnut. Home cooking at its best! *Teas served:* House Blends (India/Ceylon, India/Kenya), Indian, Darjeeling, Darjeeling and Ceylon, Assam, Kenya, Lapsang Souchong, Earl Grey, Pure China Oolong, Keemun, Rose Pouchong, Gunpowder, English Breakfast. *Fruit flavoured teas and herbal infusions are also offered.*

TETBURY GALLERY TEAROOM

Owner: Jane Maile

18 Market Place, Tetbury
Gloucestershire GL8 8DD
Tel: 01666 503412

Directions

Tetbury is ten miles from Junction 17 on the M4 and ten miles from Cirencester. The Gallery Tearoom is situated in the centre of town, just along the road, on the opposite side, to the pillared Market House.

Opening times
Open 7 days a week all year.
Times vary according to season.

Local Interest:
Walk from the tea shop to the 1655 Market House, the Georgian Parish Church of St Mary the Virgin with a spire that is the fourth highest in England. Chipping Steps was, for centuries, the site of 'Mop Fairs' where labourers, shepherds and domestic staff sought employment, and Gunstool Hill is said to have been the sight of a ducking stool and is today the venue for the weekly livestock market.

Tetbury has a history that goes back to the 7th century and many of its buildings date from the 17th and 18th centuries when it prospered as a centre for the Cotswold wool trade.

Not far from the Old Market House, the tea room is housed in the cosy drawing room of one of those elegant 18th century houses, where linen tablecloths, white china, period furniture and fine art on the walls help to create a timeless atmosphere. Jane is well known for her wonderful baking and you'll find all the traditional favourites such as coffee, chocolate, walnut, and carrot, and an unusually wide range of delicious flavoured scones, all baked on the premises. At lunchtime, the plain cheese scone makes an excellent accompaniment to a bowl of home-made soup, and the cheese and walnut wholemeal scone is wonderful with camembert and grapes. At tea time, the apricot and almond scone with jam and clotted cream is perfect with an afternoon cup of tea. If the weather is kind, a walled courtyard provides more seating. *Teas served:* Earl Grey, Lady Grey, Darjeeling, Assam, Lapsang Souchong, Ceylon, Jasmine, Rose Pouchong, decaffeinated, various fruit flavoured teas. *Herbal infusions are also offered.*

TWO TOADS

Owners: Ken and Peta Quatermass

19 Church Street
Tetbury
Gloucester GL8 8JG
Tel: 01666 503696

Directions

Two Toads is located on the Bath Road that runs from Bath to Cirencester. As you come into the village, the shop is half way between St Mary's Church and the Town Hall.

Opening times
Open all year except Christmas.
Monday–Saturday, 9 am–5 pm.
Sunday, 10 am–5 pm.

Local Interest:
In the village, visit St Mary the Virgin church and Chipping Steps. And nearby is Prince Charles' home, Highgrove, and Westonbirt, a private girls' school where the gardens and arboretum are open to the public.

Ken and Peta both gave up their jobs – Ken as an aerospace executive and Peta as a catering manager – to open Two Toads and say they have absolutely no regrets. The building in which they have created this bright sunny yellow tearoom was built in 1675 and the middle section was once a barn. The decor is light and fresh, with pale ash bentwood furniture, flowers on the tables, country and garden prints on the walls (some for sale by local artists), waitresses' aprons in green and black stripes over black uniforms and calm, elegant, easy music of the 1920s and 30s. In the beautiful courtyard garden at the back, a very popular spot for up to 30 guests in summer, there is a cherry tree, rose arch, and borders and tubs filled with plants and flowers.

The menu lists soups and jacket potatoes, pasties and quiches, filled baguettes and fresh cut sandwiches served with mixed salad leaves, and several of the products used – the cheeses, ham and fruit juices – come from local award winning suppliers. For tea time, order Cornish clotted cream to eat with scones and jam, or try the scrumpy cider cake or some of the home made produce. *Teas served:* House Morning Blend, Assam, Ceylon, Darjeeling, Earl Grey, Lapsang Souchong, China Oolong, Yunnan, Gunpowder, Jasmine, Kenya.

THE BATH SPA HOTEL

Regional General Manager:
Michael Grange

Sydney Road, Bath BA2 6JF
Tel: 0870 400 8223 Fax: 01225 444006
Website: www.bathspahotel.com

Directions
From London take the M4 and leave at junction 18. Follow the A4 into Bath city centre. At the first set of lights, turn left following signs for A36. Go over Cleveland Bridge and past the Fire Station. At the mini-roundabout, turn right, then next left after the Holburne Museum into Sydney Place. The Bath Spa Hotel is 200 yards up the hill on the right hand side.

Opening times
Open all year.

Local Interest:
Just over the river are the Abbey, Roman Baths and Pump Room, Costume Museum and No. 1, Royal Crescent, a Georgian house set in the gracious sweep of the crescent, decorated and furnished in period style. The town is full of interesting little streets and alleyways all packed with shops.

The elegance of the city of Bath is recreated in a sumptuous and traditional English style at the Bath Spa. The original mansion, a Grade I listed Georgian building, was built by a General in the Indian army who was renowned for his hospitality. The hotel continues that tradition today and despite its rather grand period style, is extremely welcoming and has a very friendly, comfortable atmosphere.

Guests have a choice of perfect locations for afternoon tea. They can choose the elegant drawing room (once the library), with its sofas, low tables and bookshelves; the muralled colonnade with its ferns and Lloyd Loom chairs and, in summer, the wonderful gardens where tables are set out under large sunshades.

The menu offers a wide selection of equally impressive real food – sandwiches, including toasted and club sandwiches – pastries, biscuits, scones and cakes that are all made in the hotel patisserie. This really is one of the most perfect places to go for afternoon tea. *Teas served:* Darjeeling, Earl Grey, Assam, Lapsang Souchong, Traditional English, Jasmine, Keemun. *Various fruit flavoured teas and herbal infusions are also available.*

LEWIS'S TEA-ROOMS

Owners: Ron and Annie Baker

**13 The High Street, Dulverton
Somerset TA22 9HB
Tel: 01398 323850**

Directions
Dulverton is on the A3223 that runs from
north west to south east across Exmoor.

It is 14 miles north of Tiverton and 25 miles
south of Minehead.

Opening times
Open all year, seven days a week.
Spring and Summer, 10 am–5.30 pm.
Winter times vary, please telephone
to confirm. 🚭

Local Interest:
*Set on the southern edge of Exmoor, Dulverton is ideally
placed for exploring the area and for visits to Somerset's
coastal towns.*

"The quintessential British Tearoom" is how one of the many delighted customers described Lewis's in the visitors' book, and this is exactly what the owners had hoped to create. This bright, spacious tearoom, set in the High Street of this attractive Exmoor town, was originally two rooms and has two fires which burn brightly in winter months. Decorated with pottery, paintings (some by the owner), brush ducks, and small antiques (many of them for sale), this primrose painted room with its wooden floor, floral tablecloths and fresh flowers is instantly welcoming. On sunny days, the small flower-filled courtyard offers the alternative of sitting outside.

Visitors are encouraged by the friendly staff to enjoy a pot of loose leaf tea or a freshly brewed cafetiere of coffee in an unhurried atmosphere, to the background of soothing classical music. As well as the irresistible selection of home made cakes prominently displayed on the centre table, there is a large choice of cream teas varied according to taste and appetite. Full English breakfasts are also available, alongside a tempting selection of rarebits – firm favourites with the customers – and traditional puddings. *Teas served:* There is a choice of over 20, including *fruit flavoured teas and herbal infusions.*

THE PUMP ROOM

Operator: Milburns Restaurants Ltd

Stall Street
Bath BA1 1LZ
Tel: 01225 444477
Fax: 01225 447979

Opening times
Open all year except Christmas Day and
Boxing Day. April–September 9 am–6 pm.
August 9.30 am–10 pm. October–March,
Monday–Saturday 9.30 am–5 pm,
Sunday 10.30 am–5 pm.
Closing times may vary slightly.
(Last admission – 30 minutes before closing.)

Directions
The Pump Room is located in the heart of the
City of Bath, adjacent to the Roman Baths, just
50 yards from Bath Abbey.

Local Interest:
*Next door are the famous Roman Baths and close by is the
Abbey, a wide range of museums, Georgian buildings and
other interesting architectural features, shops and antique
markets.*

The historic Pump Room was built by Thomas Baldwin and John Palmer between 1790 and 1795. It overlooks the King's Bath and visitors may taste the Spa waters from Britain's only geo-thermal spring from the Pump Room's Spa Fountain. This magnificent room has been a favourite meeting place since the late 18th century when fashionable society gathered there to socialise and take the waters. Today the room serves as a restaurant that offers elevenses, a selection of excellent hot and cold lunchtime dishes and a full afternoon tea menu. As well as the traditional Pump Room Tea, there is a Champagne Tea with smoked salmon sandwiches, scones with strawberry jam and clotted cream and half a bottle of champagne; there is the Tompion Tea (named after the imposing Tompion clock made by the famous clockmaker Thomas Tompion) with a selection of finger sandwiches and home made scones with jam and cream; and the High Tea which includes cheddar and stilton crostinis and a selection of cakes and pastries. Throughout the day, music is provided by The Pump Room trio or pianist who continue a three hundred year old tradition of music making in these elegant surroundings. *Teas served:* Assam, Ceylon, Darjeeling, Earl Grey, English Breakfast, Lapsang Souchong. *Herbal infusions are also available.*

SALLY LUNN'S HOUSE & MUSEUM

Owners: Jonathan Overton and
Julian Abraham

**4 North Parade Passage
Bath BA1 1NX
Tel: 01225 461634
Fax: 01225 811800
E-mail: corsham@aol.com
Website: www.sallylunns.co.uk**

Directions
Sally Lunn's is in the heart of the City of
Bath, two minutes stroll from the Abbey and
Roman Baths. Follow the street signs or ask
for directions.

Opening times
Open all year. Monday–Saturday,
10 am–11 pm. Sunday, 11 am–11 pm.
Museum: Monday–Saturday 10 am–6 pm.
Sunday 11 am–6 pm.

Local Interest:
*The Roman City of Bath is full of architectural treasures
and history – the Roman Baths, the Abbey, Royal Crescent
(a terrace of Georgian houses), the Costume Museum and
Sally Lunn's itself (the oldest house in Bath). There are
also interesting specialist shops and antique markets.*

In 1680, a young refugee by the name of Solange Luyon, arrived in Bath from France and took work with a local baker. Sally Lunn, as the locals called her, showed him how to make French brioches and the bakery became famous for the bun that took her name and which the Georgian gentry were served at public breakfasts and afternoon teas. Today, the old bakery (the oldest house in Bath) is a tea shop that still makes and serves the generous round Sally Lunn buns to the original recipe and they are delicious served as a sweet treat or as part of a savoury snack.

Half Sally Lunns are served with or as the base for most of the items on the menu. They are toasted and topped with Welsh rarebits, with smoked salmon, pate, scrambled eggs, or with jam, lemon curd, fruit compote and clotted cream; High Tea includes a bun topped with smoked salmon or sliced eggs, mayonnaise and cucumber, followed by a toasted buttered half Sally Lunn topped with generous pots of jam and clotted cream. *Teas served:* House Blend, Earl Grey, Darjeeling Moondakotte, Ceylon Mooloya, Assam Thanai, Lapsang Souchong, other blends and specialist teas. Sally Lunn's have opened a new branch in Windsor – see page 54.

THE BRIDGE TEA ROOMS

Owners: Francine and Richard Whale

24A Bridge Street, Bradford-on-Avon
Wiltshire BA15 1BY
Tel: 01225 865537

Directions
Turn immediately left after going over the bridge and park in the free town car park. Walk out of the car park and the tearooms are situated just across the narrow street in front of you.

Opening times
Open all year except Christmas Day and Boxing Day. Monday–Saturday, 9.30 am–5.30 pm. Sunday, 10.30 am–5.30 pm.

Awards
1994, 95, 97 & 99 Tea Council Award of Excellence
Egon Ronay recommended
1998 Tea Council Top Tea Place of The Year

Local Interest:
Visit the 12th century Saxon church and the tithe barn with its stone tiled roof that is said to be the largest in England, or walk along the canal and enjoy the undulating surrounding Wiltshire countryside.

Although the building that houses the Bridge Tea Rooms was constructed in 1675, the interior has been themed in Victorian style with aspidistras, 19th century china and memorabilia, including busts of Queen Victoria herself, and sepia photographs of local views and past relatives of the owner, Francine Whale. The waitresses' costumes recall the early days of London's first tearooms when white frilly aprons were worn over black dresses and white mob caps covered curls and topknots. The ambience and service are delightful, and the food is excellent.

A full afternoon tea includes sandwiches, a crumpet, a scone with thick Devon clotted cream and jam, and a cake. But if you just want a cup of tea and something sweet, there is a wide choice of really luscious cakes and patisseries that come fresh from the oven. Try a slice of carrot, banana and walnut, or choose one of the roulades – Belgian chocolate, fresh strawberry, lemon, hazelnut, pineapple or coconut. *Teas served:* House Blend, Earl Grey, Darjeeling FOP, Assam, Lapsang Souchong, Ceylon BOP, Ceylon Orange Pekoe, Kenya, Pelham, First Flush Darjeeling, Jasmine. *Fruit flavoured teas are also offered.*

POLLY TEA ROOMS

Owner: Julian West

**26–27 High Street, Marlborough
Wiltshire SN8 1LW
Tel: 01672 512146**

Directions
Marlborough is on the A4. Polly's is half way along the High Street.

Opening times
Open all year.
Monday–Friday, 8.30 am–6 pm.
Saturday, 8 am–7 pm. Sunday, 9 am–7 pm.

Awards
1985   Tea Council Top Tea Place of The Year
Egon Ronay recommended

Local Interest:
The very pretty mainly Georgian High Street is a good hunting ground for antiques and half-timbered houses in some of the back streets are very attractive. St Peter's Church has a craft centre. Nearby, visit Avebury Stone Circle and climb Silbury Hill for panoramic views of the area.

Pollys is probably one of the most important tourist attractions in Marlborough and everyone who has tea here says how wonderful it is. The shop is in a very fine bow-windowed 17th century building that was originally a house and there has been a tea shop here for over 50 years. As you walk through to the large, beamed tearoom, you are bound to be tempted by the mouthwatering array of chocolates and pastries on the counter just inside the entrance. Everything is made on the premises by local pastry chefs and you'll find it hard to decide what to choose from the long list of possibilities – macaroons, rum truffles, date slice, lemon and redcurrant cheesecake, muesli scones, Danish pastries and lots more.

Once you have made your decision, sit back and enjoy the traditional setting with its pretty flowered China, pine dressers, lace tablecloths and neatly uniformed girls who are busy all day serving tourists, schoolboys from nearby Marlborough College and their parents, and local customers who find this the perfect place to sit and relax. *Teas served:* Indian, Earl Grey, Lapsang Souchong. *Fruit infusion is also offered.*

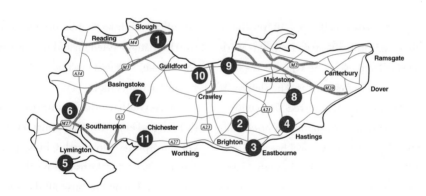

SALLY LUNN'S 1680 REFRESHMENT HOUSE

Manager: Aaron Maerhofer

11 Peascod Street
Windsor SL4 1DT
Tel: 01753 862627 Fax: 01225 811800
E-mail: corsham@aol.com
Website: www.sallylunns.co.uk

Directions
Sally Lunn's is in the centre of Windsor, just a short walk from Windsor Castle. Peascod Street is the main pedestrianised shopping street and Sally Lunn's is towards the top.

Opening times
Open all year. Monday–Saturday, 10 am–6 pm. Sunday, 11 am–6 pm.

Local Interest:
Sally Lunn's is very close to Windsor Castle and Eton. Also not far away are Frogmore House, Legoland, Savill Garden and Ascot Racecourse.

Sally Lunn's House in Bath has been a famous and successful tearoom for many years (see page 50) and the owner, Jonathan Overton, had been looking for more than ten years to find a suitable location at which to open a second shop. This new Sally Lunn's, opened in 1998, is the result of that search. It is in the conservation area of the busy town and its proximity to the castle makes it the ideal spot for sightseers and shoppers who desperately need some refreshment.

The menu and tea list is the same as at the Bath shop, so connoisseurs of the world-famous Sally Lunn buns will be delighted to be able to taste them here in Berkshire as well as Somerset. The generous, round buns (made of a semi-sweet bread that is a little like brioche) are served with sweet or savoury toppings or fillings. As in Bath, they are toasted and topped with, amongst many others, Welsh rarebits, smoked salmon, pâtes, scrambled eggs, or with chocolate butter, lemon curd, or with jam and clotted cream. The Windsor shop also has an extensive retail area specialising in fine leaf teas and tea-brewing essentials. *Teas served*: House Blend, Earl Grey, Darjeeling Moondakotte, Ceylon Mooloya, Assam Thanai, Lapsang Sourchong, other blends and speciality teas.

CLARA'S

Owner: Jane Seabrook

9 High Street, East Hoathly
Near Lewes, East Sussex BN8 6DR
Tel: 01825 840339
E-mail: claras@netway.co.uk
Website: www.netway.co.uk/users/claras

Directions
East Hoathly is just off the A22 south of
Uckfield. Clara's is in the centre of the village.

Opening times
Open all year except Mondays, Tuesdays and
two weeks 24th December–mid-January.
Monday–Tuesday, closed.
Wednesday–Saturday, 10.30 am–5 pm.
Sunday, 2–5 pm.

Local Interest:
East Hoathly's old petrol station has been converted to
workshops with furniture makers and restorers, a
traditional sign writer, a homeopathic vet, a saddlers and
tack shop, and a carpet warehouse.

The owner of this pretty tea shop, Jane Seabrook, is very interested in the history of her village and researches the family trees and histories of local village people. East Hoathly was the home of Thomas Turner, diarist and local shopkeeper and Jane sells copies of his writings which chronicle his life in the late 1700s and give a rare and detailed insight into village life in those days. Clara's itself dates from the same period, but has a Victorian facade, and inside, there are oak beams and an inglenook fireplace. In good weather, there is extra seating outside.

Upstairs there is a very interesting permanent exhibition of knitting, sewing and related memorabilia such as old sewing tools and knitting patterns and the shop sells Rowan knitting yarns, new and secondhand books, pretty cards, Sussex honey and local homemade chutneys, jams and jellies. The chutney also appears on the menu to accompany delicious rolls filled with chicken, cheese, egg mayonnaise or smoked salmon. The cake selection includes gingerbread, walnut cake and coffee sponge and teas are locally packaged. *Teas served:* Traditional Blend, Earl Grey, Darjeeling. *Herbal infusions are also offered.*

PAVILION TEA ROOMS

Owners: Coastline Caterers on behalf of Eastbourne Borough Council

Royal Parade, Eastbourne
East Sussex BN21 7AQ
Tel: 01323 410374

Directions
The Pavilion Tea Rooms is situated on the seafront, half a mile east of the pier towards the Sovereign Centre.

Opening times
Open all year (except Christmas Day).
In summer, Monday–Sunday, 10 am–6 pm.
In winter, Monday–Sunday, 10 am–5 pm.

Awards
1997 Tea Council Award of Excellence

Local Interest:
Visit the Towner Art Gallery and Museum, the Butterfly Centre on the seafront, the Lifeboat Museum, the Museum of Shops, and the Napoleonic fortress. Also good for walks along the seafront and to Beachy Head.

Pavilion Tea Rooms conjures up images of Victorian and Edwardian tea times at the seaside with pots of Lapsang Souchong or Darjeeling on the terrace while enjoying a stunning vista across the bay to Beachy Head. The setting and the style recreate everyone's idea of all the essential elements of a memorable English tea set amongst the beautiful gardens and croquet lawns – a light and elegant room, waiters who calmly bring you everything you could possibly want, newspapers for browsing through, the gentle sound of croquet and the music of the piano on summer afternoons and winter weekends, and a menu absolutely crammed with wonderful ideas to suit all tastes, at every time of the year, whatever the weather. You may choose to tuck into a cinnamon muffin or nibble at a slice of carrot and walnut cake, dip a long spoon into a raspberry meringue sundae that oozes ice cream, cream, raspberries and topped with a delicious meringue or enjoy an old fashioned cream tea or Pavilion afternoon tea.

Teas served: House Blend, Darjeeling, Earl Grey, decaffeinated, Lapsang Souchong, Estate Assam, Ceylon Orange Pekoe, Jasmine, Chamomile, kiwi and strawberry, apple and lemon.

PILGRIM'S REST

Owners: Ros and Derek Hibbert

1 High Street
Battle, East Sussex
TN33 0AE
Tel: 01424 772314

Directions
Battle lies at the junction of the A271 and the
A2100 north west of Hastings and nort east of

Eastbourne. The Pilgrim's Rest is situated on
the High Street next to Battle Abbey.

Opening times
Open all year except December 20th–
January 2nd. Open every day, 9 am–5 pm.

Local Interest:
Battle has all sorts of interesting features – 14th century
Abbey Gatehouse, medieval timber-framed and typical
Sussex weather-boarded houses, mid-16th century
Guildhall, the 12th century church of St Mary, and
beautiful South Downs countryside all around.

This Grade II listed building has housed a tea room since the late 1800s and Ros and Derek Hibbert have a charming sepia-print postcard of it in 1909 when it was still called "Pilgrims" Hospital. Dating back to 1420, it is a fine example of a medieval Wealden House, originally built by the Almoner of Battle Abbey to provide hospitality for pilgrims and travellers to the Abbey who could not afford the higher charges of the local hostelries. The building still has many of its original features, including the Kingpost, and if you look above your head you will be able to see a large area of wattle and daub that is covered in pargeting (ornamental plastering).

During the day, the Hibberts serve light lunches of such things as freshly cooked quiches, jacket potatoes, ploughman's lunches and so on. On Sunday, they offer a roast meal. Tea time brings a range of freshly baked home made scones (fruit, cheese, herb, celery and cream cheese), fruit pies, favourite cakes (including coffee and walnut, and eccles cakes). *Teas served*: Breakfast Blend, Assam, Ceylon, Darjeeling, Earl Grey, Lapsang Souchong, Rose Pouchong, lemon, decaffeinated. *Herbal infusions are also offered.*

CHEWTON GLEN

Managing Director: Peter Crome

New Milton
Hampshire BH25 6QS
Tel: 01425 275341 Fax: 01425 272310
Website: www.chewtonglen.com

Directions

From the M27 continue along the A31 for 2 ¹/₂ miles and then take a left turn signed to Emery Down. After 3 miles turn right on to the A35. Follow this for approximately

10 miles, then turn left to Walkford. Just as you are leaving Walkford, turn left into Chewton Farm Road. The hotel entrance is on the right.

Opening times

Tea is served in the conservatory every day from 3.30–6 pm. Advanced booking essential.

Award

1998 Tea Council Award of Excellence

Local Interest:

The hotel itself is a haven on the fringe of the New Forest and has 70 acres of gardens, parkland, woodland, a 9 hole golf course and tennis courts. There is also a health club with pool, gym, saunas, and steam room.

Chewton Glen is a sumptuous hotel with the peaceful and calm atmosphere of a private house that is filled with beautiful antiques and fine paintings. The house dates from the early 1700s and was remodelled in Palladian style in the early 1890s. It was here that Captain Frederick Marryat wrote: "The Children of the New Forest" in 1847 and there are pieces of Marryat memorabilia around the hotel. The lounge is an extremely elegant and tranquil room with views over the immaculate garden with its croquet lawn and colourful borders.

If you stay at the hotel, you may enjoy afternoon tea in your room, after a game of tennis or a round of golf, and this setting too gives the feeling of a comfortable private home – books on the shelves, a decanter of sherry, fresh flowers, inviting armchairs with scatter cushions and tea served on a three tier silver stand. Wherever you decide to sit, the sandwiches, scones and pastries are as perfect as surroundings. *Teas served:* Chewton Glen Blend, Assam, Darjeeling, Earl Grey, Lapsang Souchong, Orange Pekoe, Jasmine, Keemun, Gunpowder, China Oolong. *Fruit and herbal infusions are also offered.*

COBWEB TEAROOMS

Owners: Harry and Carolyn Myatt

49 The Hundred, Romsey
Hampshire SO51 8GE
Tel: 01794 516434
E-mail: cobweb-tea-rooms@barclays.net

Directions
Follow signs to Romsey off M27 or M3.
Cobweb Tearooms is the last shop at the end of the main street, 100 yards from the main entrance to Broadlands.

Opening times
Open all year except two weeks at Christmas.
Sunday and Monday closed.
Tuesday–Saturday, 10 am–5.30 pm.

Award
1996 Tea Council Award of Excellence

Local Interest:
From the tea shop, it is only a short walk to Broadlands (where Lord Mountbatten lived), the Norman abbey, King John's House and a hunting lodge. Hillier's Arboretum is three or four miles away and a 15 minute drive south takes you into the heart of the New Forest.

Cobweb Tearooms' old-world ambience is exactly right for its setting in Romsey – a charming little town with interesting antique shops, an ancient Abbey and quaint old streets. The comfortable tearoom is in a half-timbered, late 17th century building that was once an old-fashioned cobbler's shop, and the outside is today decorated with generously filled baskets that add a lovely splash of colour to the white walls. The shop's friendly environment is popular with locals who regularly pop in for a refreshing cuppa after a shopping trip, and with visitors who stop off on their way to the New Forest or after a visit to Broadlands, the home of Lord Romsey.

The paved garden at the back provides more seating and is filled with flowers – a delightful spot in which to sample some of Carolyn's home baking. The trolley is laden with pavlova, summer fruit roulade, carrot cake, and fresh fruit gateau, and in winter, there are always hot puds such as sticky toffee pudding. Or if you fancy something savoury, try the toasted sandwiches or the Cobweb Winter Tea with boiled eggs and bread and butter. *Teas served:* Assam, Darjeeling, Earl Grey, Lady Grey, Lapsang Souchong, English Breakfast, decaffeinated. *Herbal infusions are also offered.*

GILBERT WHITE'S TEA PARLOUR

Owners: The Trustees

**Gilbert White's House &
The Oates Museum
The Wakes, Selborne, Hampshire
Tel: 01420 511275   Fax: 01420 511040
E-mail: GilbertWhite@btinternet.com**

Directions

Selborne is on the B3006 which links Alton to the main A3 London to Portsmouth road. Park in the village car park behind the Selborne Arms, turn left on leaving the car park and continue along the High Street. Gilbert White's House is on the left, almost opposite the Plestor & Church.

Opening times

Open all year except 24th December–1st January. Monday–Sunday, 11 am–5 pm.

Local Interest:

Selborne is surrounded by beautiful Hampshire countryside, while at Gilbert White's House, attractions include the 18th century garden, the house itself, and the Oates Museum with exhibitions commemorating the Oates family (Captain Oates said the famous words "I am just going outside. I may be some time"). In June there is a jazz event, and an unusual plants fair, and in November, a mulled wine day offers the chance to see the house decked out for Christmas. There is also a Field Study Centre that organises courses for schools and colleges.

The Rev. Gilbert White (1720–1793) was England's first ecologist and wrote the world-famous "Natural History of Selborne". He lived here at The Wakes for most of his life and visitors can wander through the house, which is furnished in the style of his day, enjoy the glorious garden with its pond, stone ha-ha, sundial, fruit wall and fascinating collection of plants, and learn about the Oates family in The Oates Museum.

Tea is served in the dining room, added in 1794 and today decorated and furnished in period style. Many of the dishes on the menu are based on 18th century recipes, are all made on the premises and use fresh produce and herbs from the garden. At lunchtime, choose from Homity Pie, filled with creamed potato, onion and parsley topped with melted cheese, spiced potted salmon with a watercress garnish, or turkey, herb and cranberry pasty in a light pastry. And at teatime, indulge in plum cake, light madeira seed cake, 18th century scones (at the time known as Corporation Cakes), toasted wigs (spicy fruited buns) and lots more. *Teas served:* English Breakfast, Darjeeling, Ceylon, Earl Grey, Lapsang Souchong.

CLARIS'S

Owners: Brian and Janet Wingham

1–3 High Street, Biddenden
Kent TN27 8AL
Tel: 01580 291025
Website: www.clarisshop.co.uk

Directions
Biddenden lies at the junction of the A274 and A262, 12 miles south of Maidstone. The tearoom is in the centre of the village opposite the village green.

Opening times
Open all year except late January–early February. Monday, closed. Tuesday–Sunday, 10.30 am–5.20 pm.

Awards
Egon Ronay recommended

Local Interest:
Within the village, strolling visitors can discover the story of the Biddenden maids who were born joined at the hip and shoulders in 1100 and lived like that for 34 years, refusing to be separated. There are also fine examples of medieval to 17th century architecture and a 13th century church whose school is said to be haunted.

A row of picturesque 15th century weavers' houses graces the gentle bend in the unspoilt main street of this quiet Kentish village that was once the centre of the cloth trade. At the east end of the row stands Claris's tearoom and gift shop with its windows temptingly filled with Moorcroft pottery, glass, enamels, soft toys and other gifts from the selection inside, and its arched porchway that leads into the old world charm of the shop and tearoom. The low oak beams and the two inglenook fireplaces create an atmosphere of homely cosiness where lace tablecloths cover spacious tables and delicious home baked cakes and savouries are served on pretty white china.

Having settled at your table, it may take you quite a while to decide between the lemon madeira, the walnut bread served with apricot preserve, the hot bread pudding or meringue that is filled with oodles of whipped double cream from a local dairy. Or you may decide that a Scottish smoked salmon or prawn sandwich is the ideal accompaniment to your afternoon cup of tea. Whatever you choose, this is the perfect place to relax after a wander around Biddenden village or a ramble in the nearby Wealden countryside. *Teas served:* House Kenya Blend, Earl Grey, Darjeeling, Lapsang Souchong and Assam. *Fruit flavoured teas and herbal infusions are also available.*

ELAN ARTS CENTRE

Owner: Pat Fisher

Sundridge Road, Ide Hill
Near Sevenoaks, Kent TN14 6JT
Tel: 01732 750344   Fax: 01732 750476

Directions

Take the M25 to junction 5. Follow signs to Westerham (A25) and at the first set of traffic lights (in Sundridge), turn left into Church Road and continue for about two and a half miles to the top of the hill. Elan is at the roundabout facing the village green and the church.

Opening times

Open mid–February–Christmas Eve.
Monday and Tuesday, closed.
Wednesday–Sunday, 10 am–5.30 pm.

Local Interest:

Ide Hill is a reowned beauty spot, well-known by bikers, hikers, garden enthusiasts and bird watchers. Not far away is Chartwell, Hever Castle, Bough Beach Reservoir, Emmetts Garden and National Trust woodlands at Toys Hill.

Elan Arts Centre is a shoppers' paradise. The spacious 90 year old building, which used to be a grocery store and granary, now houses an ever changing display of paintings and prints by local artists, primarily watercolours featuring Kent's rural charm. There is an exceptionally large selection of fine art greetings cards and unique gift wares from around the world. And when you tire of browsing, the tearoom's hand-made wooden tables provide seating for 32 people in a light airy atmosphere where a further selection of paintings and prints interest the eye while customers enjoy coffee, lunch or tea. In warm, sunny weather, the colourful patio garden full of flowers and hanging baskets provides more space for visitors.

The menu offers an excellent choice of savoury dishes – home made soups, Elan's ploughmans, pastas, filled jackets – and delicious cakes – Austrian Moist, chocolate fudge, coffee and walnut, lemon layer, orange and elderberry, apple Dorset, carrot with apricot and walnut, toasted teacakes, shortbreads and a selection of white and wholemeal scones (fruit, cheese, apple, walnut and ginger). Holders of "The Clean Food Award" 1999–2000. *Teas served:* House Blend, Assam, Darjeeling, Earl Grey, Ceylon, Kenya, Lapsang Souchong, decaffeinated. *Herbal and fruit infusions also available.*

HASKETTS TEA & COFFEE SHOP

Owner: Emlyn Williams

86 South Street
Dorking, Surrey RH4 2EW
Tel: 01306 885833

Directions
Come into Dorking from the A24 and follow
the High Street until it splits at a Y junction.
Continue up South Street and Hasketts is

the second of two regency bow windowed
buildings on the right, 250 metres from the
Y junction.

Opening times
Open all year except Christmas Day.
Monday–Saturday, 9 am–5 pm.
Sunday, 11.30 am–5.30 pm.

Award
1999 Tea Council Award of Excellence

Local Interest:
Loseley Park, the Elizabethan seat of the ice cream
magnate is only a short distance away. Also nearby is
Polesden Lacey, the headquarters of The National Trust.

Hasketts has a home in a Grade II listed building that dates back to 1693. Situated in the sandstone cave district of Dorking, it has a basement that is actually made out of a cave and has a 220 foot well (that is now sealed off). The interior today has a 1920s-30s character and enjoys the impact of all the poster art from that period that decorates the walls. The menu has a similar nostalgia, offering lots of favourite specialities from years gone by, including eggs benedict and corned beef hash, and high tea treats such as ham carved from the bone served with cumberland sauce and a poached egg. There is also an excellent range of sandwiches and salads, and a vast selection of cakes (never less than 24 different varieties), including delicious fruit cakes which are well known abroad through the shop's export business. The tea shop is renowned for its knowledge of and enthusiasm for tea, and for the extensive range of world teas (particularly single source teas) on offer. Emlyn is so keen to share his love of the beverage that he organises educational presentations, and chats willingly to anyone who is interested. *Teas served:* 3 Assams, 3 Darjeelings, 2 Ceylons, English Breakfast, Russian Caravan, Earl Grey, Kenya, China Oolong, Gunpowder, Yunnan, Keemun, Jasmine, Rose Congou, Lapsang Souchong, Japanese, Mate, Rooibos.

SHEPHERDS TEAROOMS

Owners: Yvonne and Richard Spence

35 Little London, Chichester
West Sussex PO19 2PL
Tel: 01243 774761
E-mail: Shepherds@Shepherdtea.
freeserve.co.uk
Website: teagifts.co.uk

Directions
Little London is off East Street, one of the
main shopping streets in Chichester.

Opening times
Open all year except Sundays.
Monday–Friday, 9.15 am–5 pm.
Saturday, 8 am–5 pm. Sunday, closed.

Awards
1989, 91, 93, 96–99 Tea Council Award of Excellence
1990, 92, 95 Tea Council Top Tea Place of The Year
Egon Ronay recommended 94, 95, 96

Local Interest:
The medieval city walls, the Market Cross of 1501, the
Cathedral, Chichester District Museum and the Guildhall
are all within walking distance of Shepherds. Also nearby,
the remains of a magnificent Roman villa at Fishbourne
to the south west of the city.

Housed in a fine Georgian listed building, Shepherds has a calm, friendly, living-room atmosphere and efficient, attentive waitresses. Floral curtains, ivory walls and rich red tablecloths covered with lace set a traditional theme and the room is decorated with plants and dried flowers and there are vases of fresh flowers on the tables. The windows of the conservatory at one end flood the room with light and warmth and make this a very popular, restful venue for tourists, local business people and weary shoppers who tuck into tasty rarebits, sandwiches and scrumptious sweet treats such as Earl Grey and Sultana Cake or Coffee and Walnut Sponge. The traditional cream tea with home baked scones and generous portions of jam and cream are well worth a special visit.

Since 1987 when they acquired the tearooms, Yvonne and Richard Spence have constantly set very high standards and have researched different blends and suppliers of tea in order to offer only the best. Their special blends are so popular that they are now available via the internet or from the small shop. *Teas served:* English Breakfast, Ceylon Afternoon, Darjeeling, China Black, Earl Grey, Assam, Gunpowder, Jasmine. *Fruit flavoured teas and herbal infusions are also offered.*

LONDON

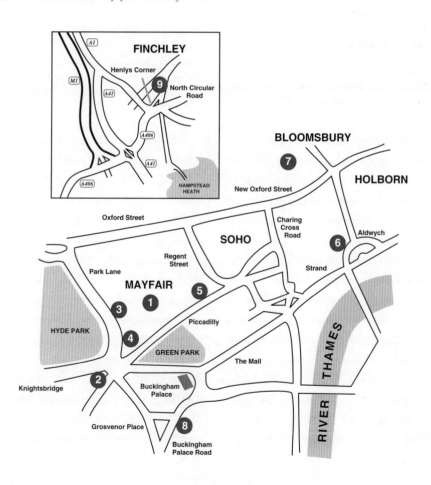

THE CHESTERFIELD

Deputy General Manager:
Richard Dixon

35 Charles Street
Mayfair, London W1X 8LX
Tel: 020 7491 2622
Fax: 020 7491 4793

Directions
The nearest underground station is Green Park on the Victoria, Jubilee and Piccadilly Lines.

Come out of the tube station into Piccadilly and walk a short distance towards Piccadilly Circus and turn left into Berkeley Street. Charles Street is the third street on the left. The hotel is on the corner of Charles Street and Queen Street, which is the second turning on the left.

Opening times
Afternoon Tea is served in the Conservatory from 3–5 pm every day.

Local Interest:
The hotel is in the heart of Mayfair, London's most exclusive area. Close by are the elegant shops of Piccadilly and Bond Street, and Buckingham Palace, Green Park and Hyde Park are just a stroll away.

The Chesterfield is more like a private club than a hotel, combining Georgian elegance and gracious living with modern standards of comfort and convenience. A crystal chandelier lights the reception area where paintings and classic leather sofas and chairs create a traditional charm. The rooms are furnished with antiques and decorated generously with fresh flowers, and the service is attentive and courteous. The Conservatory has a cool, tranquil atmosphere which is perfect for a light lunch, afternoon tea or supper before or after a West End Show. The light, "al fresco" styled room is decked with fresh flowers and plants, the tables are elegantly laid with beautiful green cloths covered with lace, the teapots, milk jugs and cake stands are silver and the food is temptingly arranged to make tea time attractive as well as delicious.

The Traditional Afternoon Tea consists of assorted finger sandwiches, freshly baked scones with clotted cream and preserves, home made fruit cakes and French pastries. Or you can simply enjoy the scones, jam and clotted cream that make up the Devonshire Cream Tea. *Teas served*: Darjeeling, English Breakfast, Orange Pekoe, Earl Grey, Lapsang Souchong, lemon, decaffeinated, Ophir Blue. *Camomile, peppermint and rosehip and hibiscus herbal infusions are also offered.*

THE CONSERVATORY AT THE LANESBOROUGH

Manager: Derek Andrews

Hyde Park Corner
London
SW1X 7TA
Tel: 020 7259 5599
Fax: 020 7259 5606

Directions
The nearest underground station is Hyde Park Corner on the Piccadilly Line. The Lanesborough is situated on the corner of Knightsbridge and Hyde Park Corner.

Opening times
Afternoon Tea is served in the Conservatory from 3.30–6 pm every day.

Local Interest:
Hyde Park Corner is close to both Hyde Park and Green Park, the elegance of Mayfair, the exclusive shops of Piccadilly and the residential charm of Belgravia.

The Lanesborough, a building that dates back to 1828, was once a fine country house that commanded magnificent views over Hyde Park. It has been meticulously restored to its original grandeur and now captures the gracious style and warm hospitality of an early 19th century residence. The glass-domed Conservatory is inspired by a chinoiserie theme and styled around the frivolity of the Brighton Pavilion. The ambience is enhanced by trickling fountains, palms and piano music that is played throughout afternoon tea. Tables are laid with elegant bone china and silver tea services, and the tea is brewed using water that has been boiled in exquisite silver samovars that stand out on view for guests to enjoy.

Afternoon Tea offers a selection of finger sandwiches, home made scones, crumpets with home made fruit preserves and Devonshire clotted cream, English tea breads and pastries. The Belgravia Tea adds fresh strawberries and cream and a glass of Taittinger Champagne or an afternoon Champagne cocktail to the full afternoon tea menu. Or you may select individual servings of any of the teatime treats or choose from a further mouthwatering menu of sandwiches and savouries, the Chef Patissier's dessert of the day, home made ice creams and sorbets. *Teas served:* Afternoon Blend, Lapsang Souchong, Earl Grey Blue Flower, Rose Congou, Darjeeling, Lychee, Ceylon, seasonal speciality estate teas.

THE DORCHESTER
THE PROMENADE
Manager: Mr F. Palminteri

Park Lane, London
W1A 2HJ
Tel: 020 7629 8888 Fax: 020 7495 7351
Website: www.dorchesterhotel.com

Directions
The Dorchester is half way up Park Lane.
Nearest tube, Marble Arch.

Opening times
Open all year.
Monday–Sunday, 8 am–1 pm.
Afternoon tea served 3–6 pm.

Awards
Egon Ronay recommended
1998 Tea Council Award of Excellence

Local Interest:
Park Lane is very close to Mayfair, Oxford Street
and Hyde Park so there are shops, cinemas, walks,
restaurants and tourist attractions.

Tea at the Dorchester is quite spectacular. No-one can fail to enjoy the elegant, yet leisurely, surroundings where marble pillars, exquisite carpets, stately plants and magnificent flowers in fine vases and planters and amazingly comfortable sofas and armchairs create around you a sense of total calm and refinement. Despite such grand style, the extremely friendly staff make sure you are relaxed and comfortable and have everything you need. The opulence of the occasion recalls the style of the very first Afternoon Teas that took place at the beginning of the 19th century in palaces and stately homes around England.

Tea in The Promenade is brought one course at a time – first the neat finger sandwiches, then the scones with Devonshire clotted cream and jam and finally pastries freshly made by the restaurant's patissier. Second and third servings are always offered but it is doubtful whether many will be able to accept further indulgences. For special occasions, choose a glass of Dorchester champagne to accompany the delicious food. *Teas served:* Dorchester House Blend, Earl Grey, Darjeeling, Assam, China Keemun, Lapsang Souchong, China Caravan, China Oolong, Jasmine, English Breakfast, Russian Caravan. *Fruit flavoured teas and herbal infusions are also offered.*

FOUR SEASONS HOTEL

Lounge Manager: Hanneke van Strik

Hamilton Place, Park Lane
London W1A 1AZ
Tel: 020 7499 0888
Fax: 020 7493 6629

Directions
The nearest tube station is Hyde Park Corner. Follow signs through the foot tunnels to the

east side of Park Lane. Hamilton Place is set back from Park Lane, running parallel to it and at right angles to Piccadilly. The entrance to the Four Seasons Hotel is a little way up on the east side.

Opening times
The Lounge is open all year.
English afternoon tea is served from 3–6 pm.

Local Interest:
Hyde Park and Green Park are both just over the road and Mayfair is just round the corner. Piccadilly offers a wide variety of shops and Knightsbridge shops are only five minutes away.

The soft recessed lighting, the palms and the exquisite Venetian chandeliers give The Lounge an extremely calm and relaxed atmosphere, and the air of tranquillity is enhanced by the gentle piano that is played live each afternoon. The walls are decorated with traditional paintings that are set in subtly lit display cabinets, and the large etched glass and wrought iron gates at one end of the room open to a garden that gives the impression of a tropical location.

The menu offers a Devonshire Tea with traditional tea sandwiches and scones, or a Seasonal Tea with speciality sandwich fillings on flavoured breads. Scones are made with nectarine, dried fruits, chestnuts, (or some similar ingredient depending on the season) and served with clotted cream and home made jams. Three delicate little pastries to suit the time of year, then follow and for a refreshing finish, there's a little chocolate cup filled with sorbet. There is always a third menu option which varies according to annual events and trends. A wide variety of coffees are served. *Teas served:* Ceylon, Assam, Darjeeling, China Black, Earl Grey, Russian Caravan, Lapsang Souchong, Gunpowder, Jasmine, Lotus, Rose Pouchong, Anniversary Blend, Queen Mary Blend. *Fruit teas and herbal infusions are also offered.*

LE MERIDIEN PICCADILLY

THE TERRACE

Manager: Thierry Iannone

21 Piccadilly
London W1V 0BH
Tel: 020 7734 8000
Fax: 020 7437 3574

Directions
Le Meridien Hotel is at Piccadilly Circus, just along the road from The Royal Academy and Burlington Arcade. The nearest tube station is Piccadilly Circus.

Opening times
The Terrace is open all year.
Tea is served every day from 3–5.30 pm.
Closed January for refurbishment.

Local Interest:
All around Piccadilly and nearby Regent Street, there are high quality shops, and not far away are Green Park, Trafalgar Square, the Mall and Buckingham Palace.

The Terrace, on the second floor of the hotel, has just been refurbished, and the use of natural materials such as limestone and timber, and the warm earthy colours of the carpets and cushions create a sense of easy comfort in an elegant, classical setting. The glass balustrade that separates the different levels, (restaurant on the upper floor and the lounge just below with a view over Piccadilly), and the mirrored walls give a floating upper feeling of space and light. The new afternoon tea chef, Christophe Prud'homme, is excited by the variations of flavour that tea offers and is creating recipes that include different sorts of tea in unusual ways.

The afternoon tea menu offers the traditional selection of sandwiches, scones with home made seasonal jams, and pastries; the De Luxe Afternoon Tea adds a glass of champagne and an ice cream, sorbet, or fresh fruit as a fourth course; and the children's tea allows parents to introduce the younger generation to the joys of tea time with special favourites such as marshmallows and milkshakes. The relaxed elegance is enhanced by live music from the 30s and 40s every Friday, Saturday and Sunday. *Teas served:* Assam, Ceylon, Darjeeling, China Oolong, Keemun, Gunpowder, Earl Grey, Jasmine, Traditional English, Lapsang Souchong, Vanilla. *Herbal infusions are also offered.*

LE MERIDIEN WALDORF

PALM COURT

Palm Court Manager: Mr Osman El-Tahlawi

Aldwych, London WC2B 4DD
Tel: 020 7836 2400
Fax: 020 7836 7244

Directions
Nearest tube stations are Holborn, Covent

Garden, Temple or Charing Cross. Buses that go to Aldwych are: 1, 9, 11, 13, 15, 23, 26, 68, 76, 77A, 91, 168, 171, 171A, 188, 501, 505, 521.

Opening times
Open all year.
Tea is served Monday–Friday, 3–5.30 pm.
Tea Dances, Saturday, 2.30–5 pm.
Sunday, 3.30–6.30 pm.

Local Interest:
Covent Garden, Royal Opera House, several major theatres, the City of London, and a short walk away over Waterloo Bridge lies the South Bank complex with concert halls, art galleries, theatres and museums.

The Waldorf Hotel opened its doors in 1908 and very quickly became a favourite place for an elegant and refined afternoon tea. In 1910 the Tango arrived from Buenos Aires and prompted the beginning of that rather eccentric mix of Argentine dancing and English tea drinking – the Tea Dance. By 1913, the Waldorf's golden and white ballroom was one of London's most popular venues for Tango Tea Dances.

Today, tea is served in the magnificent Palm Court where exotic plants, a marble terrace, gentle Edwardian colours and twinkling lights create a unique setting for a stylish tea or tea dance. The menu suggests a three course tea with sand-wiches (including prawn Marie Rose on citrus bread, cream cheese and chives with cucumber on raisin and pecan bread, turkey with mustard grain mayonnaise on rye bread), fruit and plain scones, and neat little slices of tiramisu, chocolate mille feuilles, or passion fruit cheesecake. The Friday 'Unlimited Chocolate Buffet' is irresistible to chocolate lovers. Tea Dances are sparkling occasions for both dance and tea enthusiasts. Indulge in slow elegant waltzes, energetic jives and cha cha chas, or the sultry steps of a tango. *Teas served:* Waldorf Blend, Assam, Darjeeling, Ceylon, Earl Grey, Jasmine, Kenya, Lapsang Souchong, mint iced tea. *Herbal infusions are also available.*

71

THE MONTAGUE ON THE GARDENS

Manager: Tricia Fitzsimons

15 Montague Street
Bloomsbury, London WC1B 5BJ
Tel: 020 7637 1001
Fax: 020 7637 2516

Directions

The nearest tube station is Russell Square. From the tube station, go into the square by the gate closest to the tube station and head diagonally across the square. Turn into Montague Street and the hotel is a little way down on the left hand side. From the main entrance of the British Museum, turn left along Great Russell Street and take the first left into Montague Street.

Opening times

Afternoon tea is served in the lounge or on the terrace every day from 3–6 pm.

Local Interest:

The Montague is very close to the British Museum, the University of London and the shops of Oxford Street.

The Montague Hotel is set in a Grade II listed building that was originally built in 1675 as part of the Bloomsbury Estate, begun by the 5th Duke of Bedford and continued by the 6th Duke on the site of Bedford House. Part of the terrace of buildings developed then, now houses the Georgian fronted hotel. The name is taken from Ralph, the Duke of Montague whose portrait still hangs in the foyer today. The hotel has an intimate atmosphere, and a genteel afternoon tea is served in the elegant lounge (with its country house décor, chandeliers and the richly coloured soft furnishings), or on the terrace, beneath large sunshades and overlooking peaceful gardens.

The pretty traditional china and the silver three tier cake stand set the scene for a classic afternoon tea of finger sandwiches, scones and pastries of the day, or a Cream Tea with scones and Devonshire clotted cream, jam and a pot of tea. The menu provides a brief history of tea as "invented" by the Duchess of Bedford and a description of the teas on offer. *Teas served:* Assam, Ceylon, Darjeeling, Earl Grey, Jasmine, Keemun, Lapsang Souchong, green teas from China and Japan. *Herbal infusions are also offered.*

RUBENS AT THE PALACE

General Manager: Jonathan Raggett

**39–41 Buckingham Palace Road
London SW1W 0PS
Tel: 020 7834 6600
Fax: 020 7828 5401**

Directions

The nearest tube station is Victoria on the Victoria, District and Circle lines. Come out of Victoria station and turn right into Buckingham Palace Road. The Rubens is between Victoria Street and Palace Street, opposite the Royal Mews.

Opening times
Afternoon tea is served in the Palace Lounge every day from 2.30–5 pm.

Local Interest:
Within a few minutes' walk are Buckingham Palace, St James's Park, Green Park, and the Mall. Westminster Cathedral, Westminster Abbey and the Houses of Parliament are only a short walk away.

The Rubens Hotel's Cavalry Bar and Palace Lounge, in keeping with the location opposite the Royal Mews (that stands at this south west corner of the grounds of Buckingham Palace) have just been refurbished with a royal theme. The hotel is so close to Buckingham Palace that you only have to walk a very short distance before you are standing gazing into the famous royal forecourt, and the hotel has a splendid view of the arrivals and departures to and from the Mews itself. After a walk or jog in Green Park, or a stroll up the Mall or to the Houses of Parliament in Westminster Square; what could be better than to relax in such luxurious surroundings and take tea?

When you take Afternoon Tea at The Rubens you will enjoy a selection of delicate finger sandwiches (filled with smoked salmon, cream cheese and cucumber, egg mayonnaise, and ham), freshly baked scones with clotted cream or toasted teacakes, and little cakes that include chocolate eclairs, fresh fruit tartlets and fruit cakes. The all-day menu offers English and continental-style breakfasts, snacks and light meals, main dishes and desserts to suit all palates. *Teas served:* Assam, Darjeeling, Earl Grey, Indian Blend, House Blend, iced tea. *Fruit and herbal infusions are also offered.*

THE TEA HOUSE

Owner: Su Russell

College Farm
45 Fitzalan Road
London N3 3PG
Tel: 020 7240 9571
Fax: 020 7836 3893

Directions
The nearest tube station is Finchley Central.
Turn left out of the station, walk to the end of
the road and turn left into Regents Park Road.

Walk about ¼ mile and turn right into Fitzalan
Road. By road, turn off the North Circular
Road at Henlys Corner (junction with Finchley
Road) into Regents Park Road. Fitzalan Road is
off to the left.

Opening times
Open every Sunday, 2–6 pm.
Selected tea parties on other days.
Closed December and January.

Local Interest:
*College Farm still has cattle, sheep, pigs, goats, poultry,
donkeys, etc. Entrance charge: Adults £1.50, Children 75p,
Concessions £1.25.*

There has been a farm on this site since medieval times. Originally a sheep farm, it was bought in 1868 by the founder of the Express Dairy, G. T. Barham, who redesigned it in 1882 as a working dairy. In 1920, the dairy was turned into a tearoom but sadly, by the early 1980s, had become a rather shabby refreshments room. Then Su Russell became involved and she spent many lonely hours scraping determinedly at the seven layers of paint and paper that concealed the old Minton tiles. Working from a 1920s photograph, she has restored the room to its original charm, with bentwood chairs, chequered floor and tables decorated with linen cloths and fresh flowers.

It has taken Su years to collect the distinctive Willow Pattern tea services and treasures have been given by friends and customers, or hunted out from antique shops. Other 'finds' that add to the feel of nostalgia have been gratefully accepted – Express Dairy tea towels, an old till and an early ice-cream maker. Now Su serves home made scones with jam and Devon clotted cream (sent up by train every Sunday from Budleigh Salterton) in this delightful little time warp. *Teas served:* Indian, China, teas from Russia, Malawi, Thailand, Egypt, Singapore, Japan, Zanzibar, decaffeinated. *Fruit flavoured teas and herbal infusions are also offered.*

E A S T
R E G I O N A L   M A P

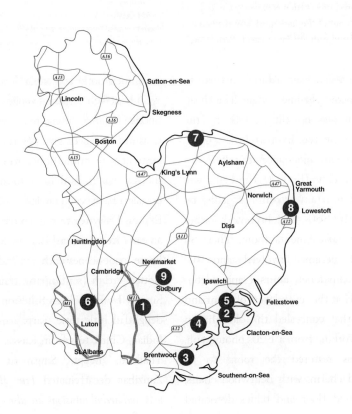

THE CAKE TABLE TEAROOM

Owner: Rachel Mead

5 Fishmarket Street, Thaxted
Essex CM6 2PG
Tel: 01371 831206

Directions
Thaxted is well signposted on the B1051
and B184. The tearoom is tucked away to
the left of the Guildhall.

Opening times
Open all year during winter months except for
Christmas and Annual Holidays. Monday,
closed. Tuesday–Sunday, 11 am–5 pm.
Open Bank Holidays. Please telephone for
winter mid-week opening hours.

Awards
1990 & 97   Tea Council Award of Excellence
1991   Tea Council Top Tea Place of The Year
1993–96   Egon Ronay recommended

Local Interest:
Thaxted Guildhall was built in 1390. The town
is also famous for its medieval church and windmill.

One of Kathleen Albon's customers recently described her visit to The Cake Table as "just like being at home". The Albons have certainly achieved a very homely, old-fashioned atmosphere, with old beams, chintz curtains and furnishings, white china, an open fire, classical music and lots of really good home baking – coffee and walnut, traditional bread pudding and the scones being the most popular. The interior is so traditionally English and attractive that film crews have used the tea shop as the setting for television dramas and the stars have themselves stopped for tea.

Kathleen serves a very interesting range of well-known and more obscure teas from around the world. The menu gives valuable information about the taste and benefits of these and some, displayed on the dresser, are for sale. The shop also sells tea cosies, locally made hand-smocked aprons and floral prints by a local artist. In good weather, there is additional seating in the pretty walled garden where hanging baskets continue the theme of old world charm. *Teas served:* House Blend, Assam, Darjeeling, Earl Grey, English Breakfast, Keemun, Kenya, Lapsang Souchong, Yunnan, Russian Caravan, Oolong, Gunpowder, Japanese Sencha, Lychee, decaffeinated, organic, iced tea on summer days. *Fruit flavoured teas and herbal infusions are also offered.*

POPPYS TEA ROOMS

Owners: Antony and Anita Benton

17 Trinity Street, Colchester
Essex CO1 1JN
Tel: 01206 765805

Directions

Take the A12 from the M25 and follow to Colchester. Poppys is in the town centre close to the Clock Museum.

Opening times
Open all year.
Monday–Thursday, 9.30 am–5 pm.
Friday and Saturday, 9.30 am–5.30 pm.
Sunday, closed.

Awards
Egon Ronay recommended

Local Interest:
Poppys is set in the old part of Colchester that has not been spoilt by large modern buildings. It is surrounded by narrow streets and Roman ruins. Colchester is Britain's oldest recorded town.

Poppys gets a lot of visits from foreign tourists and one group wrote in the guest book, "We didn't expect such big meals in such a small restaurant – we will be back!" It is small, but its large reputation as being the best in Colchester has spread beyond the immediate locality because of its charming Victorian style and the delicious food. The building is full of old beams and Victorian bric-a-brac, with relaxing classical music playing in the background and the staff wear period uniforms with mop caps.

As well as a very wide range of all day dishes – quiches, hot jacket potatoes, pastas and pies – there is an excellent choice of hot and cold sandwiches – honey roast ham with cheese, prawn mayonnaise, mackerel and orange, pork sausage, BLT, the ultimate cucumber sandwich and CBLT. And, for the health conscious, the menu includes large helpings of seasonal mixed salads and home made soups. Tea time brings six set menus with sandwiches, scones, croissants, crumpets, teacakes, and a whole host of cakes and puddings known as Poppys Pudding Club! *Teas served:* Darjeeling, Earl Grey, English Breakfast, Yorkshire, Lapsang Souchong, Lady Grey, Assam. *Fruit flavoured teas and herbal infusions are also available.*

SQUIRES

Owners: Helen and Carl Watson

11 High Street
Rayleigh
Essex SS6 7EW
Tel: 01268 741791

Directions

Rayleigh is situated on the A129 within easy access of the A127. Squires is located at the upper end of the High Street close to Trinity Church.

Opening times

Open all year except Sundays.
Monday–Saturday, 9 am–5.30 pm.
Sunday, closed.

Local Interest:

Close to the tearoom is a windmill that stands on a mount, and two or three minutes away is a Dutch Cottage that is lived in but is open on certain days to the public.

The 300-year-old building that houses Squires is one of only a few original buildings in this busy high street. Old wooden beams run across the ceiling and a red brick fire place gives the tearoom a traditional atmosphere. Bentwood chairs, dark wooden tables and a professional standard of service, carry this through. Both Helen and Carl gave up a career at sea to open Squires, and Helen has a strong link with tea since her father once worked for a major tea importing company. They have created a really friendly, welcoming atmosphere where locals pop in regularly for lunch or tea.

Nearly all of the items on the menu are home made and there is an extensive range of lunchtime savouries (soups, toasted muffin topped with melting cheese, bacon and tomato; croissants filled with cheese and ham or scrambled egg and bacon, various rarebits), sandwiches, and cakes and puddings. The most popular of the sweet dishes are the fruit crumbles, pear and almond torte, banoffee pie and strawberry cheesecake. Squires serves a selection of 25 loose leaf teas which include: Ceylon, Assam, First Flush Darjeeling, Second Flush Darjeeling, English Breakfast, Kenya, Keemun, Black Dragon Oolong, Jasmine Monkey King, Earl Grey, Lapsang Souchong, Advent of Winter, Tea of Life green tea. *Herbal and fruit infusions are also offered.*

TEA ON THE GREEN

Owner: Mick Hellier

3 Eves Corner, Danbury
Essex CM3 4QF Tel: 01245 226616

Directions
Leave the M25 at Junction 28 and take the
A12 towards Chelmsford. By-pass Chelmsford
and then take the A414 off the A12 to Maldon.
Danbury is approximately 5 miles along this
road. When you reach the village green, turn
left into Little Baddow Road and then straight
on to the tearoom.

Opening times
Open all year except Christmas and New Year.
In summer, Monday–Friday, 8.30 am–5 pm.
Saturday, 10 am–5 pm. Sunday, 11 am–5 pm.
In winter, Monday–Friday, 8.30 am–5 pm.
Saturday, 10 am–4.30 pm. Sunday, 11 am–
4.30 pm. Bank Holidays, 11 am–6 pm.

Award
1999 Tea Council Award of Excellence

Local Interest:
The land immediately surrounding the tearoom is
National Trust property and so is open for walking. Blakes
Wood and Danbury Lakes and Common are also popular
with walkers and just north of Danbury is Woodham
Water where there is a nature trail.

The large pink building that houses this delightful tearoom overlooks the village green and duck pond set in National Trust land. Inside, the décor is soft pastel colours, floral table cloths and fine white bone china and has a cricket and golf theme – which always provokes comments and conversation from guests. There are also numerous teapots of all shapes and sizes displayed around the room and a collection of books on tea and coffee for customers to browse through. The atmosphere is relaxing and fun.

The informative menu offers a good selection of breakfast and light lunchtime dishes and an excellent range of tea-time toasts, breads and scones. As well as traditional hot buttered crumpets, English muffins and cinnamon toast, you can also choose waffles with maple syrup, cinnamon muffins or toasted bagels. The house special 'Tea On The Green' afternoon tea includes a choice of tasty finger sandwiches, a sultana scone with cream and strawberry jam and a slice of cake. For children there are small portions at reduced prices and an imaginative list of treats, with 'Mouse Trap' (cheese sandwich plus drink and cake), 'Flipper' (tuna sandwich), 'Monkey Business' (banana sandwich) adding to the fun. *Teas served:* English Breakfast, Afternoon Blend, Earl Grey, Lady Grey, Jasmine, Assam, Darjeeling, Ceylon, Lapsang Souchong, decaffeinated. *Herbal and fruit infusions are also offered.*

TRINITY HOUSE TEAROOM & GARDEN

Managers: Ray and Heather Ablett

47 High Street
Manningtree
Essex
CO11 1AH
Tel: 01206 391410
Fax: 01206 391216

Directions
Take the A137 from Ipswich, or the A131 from Colchester into the centre of Manningtree.
Trinity House is situated in the main street.

Opening times
Open all year, including Easter.
Monday–Saturday, 9 am–4.30 pm.

Local Interest:
The tearoom overlooks the River Stour with its boating area, also close by are The Walls, a grassed walking area along the river – a good point from which to view birds and wild fowl and a favourite spot for artists.

Trinity House Tearoom is run to help support and provide work for the residents of Acorn Village – a community within Manningtree for people with learning disabilities. A great deal of care and thought goes into the organisation of the tea shop and its menu. Trinity House holds the local council's Hygiene Award and Heartbeat Award for healthy living and healthy options include all sorts of lunchtime savoury dishes, filled rolls and sandwiches. There's a tempting array of home made cakes (including indulgent treats such as lemon meringue pie with cream, Danish pastries and fruit pies with custard, ice cream or cream) and fat free teabreads and sponge cakes.

The tearoom is on the scenic Coastal Route from Harwich, in a prime position in Manningtree where Matthew Hopkins, witchfinder general is said to have operated in the seventeenth century. The popular Essex Way is also nearby and Manningtree is a favourite stop for cyclists and walkers. The beautiful Tea Garden is entered each year in the local Floral Manningtree Competition in conjunction with Anglia in Bloom. *Teas served:* A very wide variety including House Blend, Yorkshire Blend, Assam, Earl Grey, Lady Grey, Darjeeling, Lapsang Souchong, English Breakfast, decaffeinated, iced teas. *Fruit flavoured teas and herbal infusions are also available.*

THE TEA & COFFEE HOUSE

Owner: Shirley Davies

6/7 Market Place
Hitchin, Herts SG5 1DR
Tel: 01462 433631

Directions
The Tea & Coffee House is located in the town centre on the Market Place Square.

Opening times
Open all year except Sunday.
Monday–Saturday, 9.30 am–5.30 pm with last orders taken at 5 pm. 🚭

Awards
1997 Tea Council Award of Excellence

Local Interest:
Hitchin is a beautiful market town. Many local features include an open market on Tuesday, Friday and Saturday; a Victorian chemist shop housed in the museum; and a physic garden alongside.

The Tea & Coffee House is a privately owned business which started as a shop selling specialist teas and coffees in 1986. In 1993, the business moved to larger premises where a seating area serving teas and coffees was created alongside. In May 1996 the business again expanded to its new central location and now offers the customer a sense of space and light with huge picture windows overlooking the main market square. Classical music is played and the daily papers are provided for customers' enjoyment.

The range of teas gives an almost unique opportunity for customers to sample and buy really unusual blends and speciality teas and coffees.

The food is of as high a quality as the beverages with all food freshly prepared to order and all cakes hand-made.

The staff are extremely helpful with advice about which tea to order, and, when you have found one you like, you can buy more from the counter to take home or give as a gift. *Teas served:* 70 different varieties including a House Blend (Assam & Kenya), Darjeeling, Assam, Ceylon, Kenya, China Silver Tip Oolong, Ceylon, African, China, Japanese, decaffeinated and exotic flavoured teas. *Fruit flavoured teas and herbal infusions are also available.*

SHRUBLANDS OF WIGHTON

Owners: Graham and Susan Polson

Shrublands, Wells Road, Wighton
Wells-Next-The-Sea, Norfolk NR23 1PR
Tel: 01328 820743 Fax: 01328 820088
E-mail: shrublands@shrub-lands.
freeserve.co.uk

Directions
From Wells-Next-The-Sea, take the A149
towards Cromer and follow signs to Warham,
Wighton and Little Walsingham. Shrublands is

on the left in Wighton. From Fakenham, take the
A148 towards Cromer, then the B1105 towards
Wells-Next-The-Sea. Turn right to Barsham and
Little Walsingham and continue to Wighton.
Shrublands is on the right hand side in the village.

Opening times
Open from Easter to the end of September.
Monday, Thursday, closed. Tuesday, Wednesday,
Friday, Saturday, Sunday, 12 noon–5 pm. October
to Christmas, open Saturday and Sunday,
12 noon–4 pm. Bank Holidays, open but closed the
following day. Christmas–Easter, closed.

Local Interest:
*Wighton is only 3 miles from the north Norfolk coast and
close to Warham Hill Fort and the Wells and Walsingham
Light Railway.*

Shrublands of Wighton is a guest house and tearoom where a pretty, vaulted and beamed dining room provides seating for up to twenty guests for lunch, tea or dinner parties. The older features are not obvious from the outside of the building but once inside, visitors find themselves in a charming room with cottage style chairs and tables, starched tablecloths, a country atmosphere and a really warm, friendly service. There are no pre-packed tubs of jam or plastic tables here. Everything is done 'properly' and the Polsons try to ensure that each and every guest is individually welcomed with courtesy and consideration.

All the cakes, tea breads and savouries are baked on the premises – and even when Sue broke her leg in five places in 1999 and spent several weeks in a wheelchair, everything continued as normal, with part-time staff and the Polsons' two sons rallying round. The tearoom serves light lunches and traditional tea-time sandwiches, tea cakes, scones with jam and cream, and a range of cakes, pastries and biscuits. The menu also includes more than 30 different teas. *Teas served:* Yorkshire Gold, Assam, Darjeeling, Earl Grey, Lady Grey, Lapsang Souchong, Jasmine, Gunpowder, Yunnan, Russian Caravan and many more. *Herbal infusions are also offered.*

FLYING FIFTEENS

Owners: Peter and Diana Knight

19a The Esplanade, Lowestoft
Suffolk NR33 0QG
Tel: 01502 581188
Fax: 01502 586991

Directions
The tea shop is located on the sea front promenade of the South Beach between the South Pier and the Claremont Pier, near to the Hatfield Hotel.

Opening times
Easter–Spring Bank Holiday:–Weekends only.
Spring Bank Holiday:–Mid October,
Tuesday–Sunday, 10.30 am–5 pm.
Closed Mondays except Bank Holidays.
Mid October–Easter, closed.

Award
1999 Tea Council Award of Excellence

Local Interest:
Lowestoft is the most easterly point of the British Isles and the golden sands of its safe South Beach have received national recognition. A traditional family resort with the Harbour and Yacht Marina close by. There are local museums in North Lowestoft and Oulton Broad, the gateway to the Norfolk Broads, which is nearby.

The unusual name for this delightful tearoom comes from the Flying Fifteen sailing boats that can regularly be seen racing out of the nearby Yacht Club. The boat was designed by Uffa Fox in 1947 and in his book 'Sailing Boats' there is an interesting account of how he took Prince Philip's Flying Fifteen 'Cowslip' to the 1958 Lowestoft June Regatta.

A great deal of thought has gone into the design of the tearoom and the light décor of pale yellow and pale turquoise reflects the colours of sea and sand. Customers can also sit in the attractive seafront garden which has won several gold awards in the 'Lowestoft in Bloom' competition. The simple menu has been very carefully put together and everything is beautifully presented on china designed by Jeff Banks. Sandwich fillings include locally produced ham or smoked salmon; the scones, which include special strawberry scones draw compliments all the time and the cakes, all of which are made on the premises, are always popular – especially the boozy fruit cake and strawberry meringues.

Since opening in 1996 Flying Fifteens has gained a reputation for delicious food and excellent service. *Teas served:* Over 25 different teas including Assam, Darjeeling, English Breakfast, Earl Grey, Ceylon. *Fruit and herbal infusions are also available.*

THE SWAN

General Manager: Beth Raine

High Street, Lavenham
Sudbury, Suffolk
CO10 9QA
Tel: 01787 247477
Fax: 01787 248286

Directions
Lavenham is on the A1141 between Bury
St Edmonds and Hadleigh. The Swan is

located in the centre of the medieval village
of Lavenham.

Opening times
Open all year.
Tea is served in the lounge from
3 pm–5.30 pm.

Local Interest:
*In the Middle Ages, Lavenham was the centre of the wool
trade and one of the wealthiest towns in England. Walk
from The Swan to the medieval Guildhall (National
Trust), the Priory, the Little Hall and the cathedral-like
Church of St Peter and St Paul.*

In the 15th century, four timbered houses in the centre of this incredibly unspoilt and picturesque town were united to form the Swan Hotel and today it is still a hotel of great character and charm and a perfectly wonderful place to stop for a traditional English tea. The cosy, comfortable lounge has quaint snug corners that are ideal for a quiet, refined cup of tea, open fireplaces where roaring log fires crackle their welcome in winter months, generous arrangements of fresh and dried flowers all over the room and a lovely view of the walled, cloistered garden with its lawn surrounded by pretty borders. In

summer, customers spill out into this beautiful space for their three course tea that is served on silver, tiered cake stands, or a cream tea with home-baked scones, home-made jams and Cornish clotted cream.

At weekends, the old-world atmosphere of refinement and gentle pleasure is enhanced by harpsichord recitals. You will feel as if you have settled into a genteel country house where afternoon refreshment is an essential part of each day's enjoyment. *Teas served:* House Blend, Earl Grey, Assam, Darjeeling, Lapsang Souchong.

MIDDLE ENGLAND
REGIONAL MAP

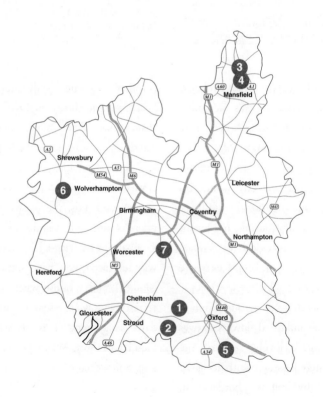

THE BAY TREE

Owner: Christine O'Neill

1 Victoria Street
Bourton-on-the-Water, Cheltenham
Gloucestershire BL54 2BT
Tel: 01451 821818

Directions
Follow the A429 from Stow-on-the-Wold and
turn left into Bourton. Victoria Street runs off
the main high street, and the Bay Tree is

approximately 100 yards from the famous
Cotswold Perfumery. Access is by any of the
bridges over the river.

Opening times
Open all year. Summer opening times vary.
Monday–Thursday, 10 am–late evening.
Friday and Saturday, 9 am–late evening.
Sunday, 10 am–8 pm.

Local Interest:
Bourton-on-the-Water is one of the larger Cotswold
villages and has many beautiful buildings in mellow
Cotswold stone. There is also a model village, a model
railway, the Cotswold Perfumery and a Motor Museum.

This pretty tea shop is housed in one of Bourton's typical picturesque honey-coloured stone buildings, and once inside you will find a traditional tea room atmosphere with dark wood furniture, flower prints on the walls, fresh flowers on each table and a menu offering traditional meals throughout the day. The emphasis is on individual friendly service and a menu that offers healthy options. The Baytree has won Heartbeat awards for the range of low fat meals (low fat cheese salad, broccoli and cheese bake, mushroom stroganoff) and vegetarian dishes (vegetable curry, tomato pasta, vegetable chilli) that Christine O'Neill offers. At teatime, cream teas are served with fruit scones and Cornish clotted cream, and the Baytree Special Cream Tea includes sandwiches, scones and a slice of cake. When you've finished lunch or afternoon tea, why not wander into the Baytree's shop next door and browse amongst the wide selection of collectable teapots, speciality teas and coffees that offer something to suit everyone's taste, and other tea paraphernalia. *Teas served*: Traditional English Blend, Cotswold Blend, Earl Grey, Darjeeling, Assam, Ceylon, Yunnan, Lapsang Souchong, Jasmine, lemon, iced teas. *Herbal and fruit infusions are also offered.*

THE BLACK CAT

Owners: Mark and Margaret O'Donohoe

High Street
Lechlade on Thames
Gloucestershire BL7 3AD
Tel: 01367 252273

Directions
Follow signs to the centre of Lechlade. From Market Square continue along the High Street past the post office, The Red Lion and Thames Street which runs off to the left. The Black Cat is a little further along on the left hand side.

Opening times
Open all year except Mondays.
Monday, closed. Tuesday–Friday,
9.30 am–5 pm. Saturday, 9.30 am–5.30 pm.
Sunday, 10 am–5.30 pm.

Local Interest:
Lechlade is a gently bustling market town beside green riverside meadows. It has many antique shops and craft galleries, a 15th century church, and a riverside pub and marina. Also in the locality are Lechlade Trout Farm, Cotswold Woollen Mill/Museum and Cotswold Wildlife Park.

The Black Cat is a very successful combination of a specialist tea and coffee retail operation and a fully fledged tearoom which gives customers the chance to sample any of the shop's teas, tisanes and coffees before choosing which one to buy to take home. As an independent family business, the O'Donohoes feel that they offer an old-fashioned standard of service that is sadly missing from so many catering outlets today. Their menu contains an excellent range of traditional savouries (ploughmans with various cheeses, rarebits, sandwiches and daily specials such as deep fried brie salad and duck and bacon pie), there are special options for children, and for tea there are scones, tea cakes, and a variety of cakes from the trolley.

The shop also sells a wide range of tea and coffee making equipment and accessories and offers advice as to which leaf teas and coffee beans will suit different customers' requirements. They also give advice as to how to brew them. Above the shop is a holiday apartment that sleeps four and is available to let on a weekly basis. *Teas served:* English Breakfast, 2 Darjeelings, Assam, 2 Ceylons, Earl Grey, Keemun, Lapsang Souchong, Jasmine Gunpowder, Russian Caravan, Formosa Finest Oolong, Rose Congou, Japanese Genmaicha, fruit flavoured teas. *Fruit tisanes and herbal infusions are also offered.*

OLDE SCHOOL TEAROOM

Owner: Gwen Elliott

**Carburton, Near Worksop
Nottinghamshire S80 3BP
Tel: 01909 483517**

Directions

Carburton is on the B6034 that runs from Worksop to Allerton. The Olde School Tearoom is at the crossroads with the road that runs from Clumber Park to Norton village.

Opening times
Open all year except January.
Monday, closed.
Tuesday–Friday, 10 am–4.30 pm.
Saturday and Sunday, 10 am–5 pm.

Award
1992   Tea Council Award of Excellence

Local Interest:
The Olde School is opposite one of the entrances to Clumber Park and as Carburton is in the middle of Sherwood Forest it is an excellent area for walks. At nearby Edwinstow is the Sherwood Forest Visitor Centre and at Newark, an interesting castle.

Many of the regular customers in this converted 1930s school are local people who love the peace and quiet of a country tearoom. But it is also an ideal place for tourists after a drive or ramble in Sherwood Forest or Clumber Park. Gwen Elliott has preserved the spirit of the school building and has an old school desk in the entrance, her menu written up on the blackboard and easel and the original children's hand basins in the wash rooms. The old school shelves, once used for reference books and stacks of homework, now display woodwork, greeting cards and handmade prints by local artists. The partition that in the past divided the main classroom into two is now used to make a separate room for private parties, and the old school bell is still available to attract the attention of large groups if they are being too jolly and making too much noise!

Good service and value are important to Gwen and her menu offers a very reasonably priced selection of home made savouries, cakes and freshly cut sandwiches. The most popular cake is something her mother used to make when Gwen was a child – a fruit slice with a pastry base, a layer of jam and topping of sponge full of dried fruits. *Teas served:* House Blend, Assam, Darjeeling, Earl Grey, Ceylon.

OLLERTON WATER MILL TEA SHOP

Owners: Kate and Ellen Mettam

Ollerton Mill, Market Place
Ollerton, Newark
Nottinghamshire NG22 9AA
Tel: 01623 824094/822469

Directions
Ollerton lies at the junction of the A614 and B616, between Worksop and Nottingham. The

Water Mill and Tea Shop are in the centre of the village, almost opposite the church.

Opening times
Open March–mid November. Tuesday–Sunday, 10.30 am–5 pm. Open every Bank Holiday and any other time by arrangement. 🚭

Awards
1994, 95 & 99 Tea Council Award of Excellence

Local Interest:
The mill has an exhibition with colourful display panels which tell the story of the mill. There is also a video which shows the mill grinding and producing flour.

Ollerton is situated on the edge of Sherwood forest in a corner of rural England that has remained unchanged for three hundred years, and the Mill, built in 1713, stands on the same spot as the medieval mill that is mentioned in the Domesday Book. Since 1921, it has been in the Mettam family who have been millers for many generations and whose family tree has been traced back to 1635. In 1993, it was lovingly restored by them and now sisters-in-law, Kate and Ellen Mettam, run the tea shop which is housed in the Old Millwright's workshop. The entrance has a wonderful view of the waterwheel and mill race and the

tea shop itself looks directly over the River Maun. This is a delightful spot and visitors have the chance to learn a little about what life was like for a working miller in the 18th century while at the same time enjoying a really special afternoon tea. All the cakes, quiches and mouth-watering puddings are baked on the premises with flour that is sold in the mill. The Ollerton Mill Cream Tea is just perfect – three dainty fruit or plain scones served with lashings of jam and cream. *Teas served:* House Blend, Earl Grey, Assam, Darjeeling, Lady Grey. *Fruit and herbal infusions are also offered.*

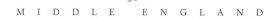

ANNIE'S TEA ROOMS

Owner: Jean Ann Rowlands

79 High Street
Wallingford
Oxfordshire OX10 0BX
Tel: 01491 836308

Directions

Wallingford is situated at the junction of the A329, Reading to Oxford road, and the A4130, Henley to Wantage road. Annie's is in the High Street, just along from the crossroads with St Martin's Street and Castle Street.

Opening times

Open all year except Sundays, Wednesdays and Bank Holidays. Monday, Tuesday, Thursday–Saturday, 10 am–5 pm.

Local Interest:

The castle grounds are excellent for walks and hold concerts on summer Sundays. There is a regatta in May, a carnival in June and a Victorian celebration in December when the entire town participates in entertainments and markets.

Wallingford's history goes back to the granting of its charter in 1155 and it has links with a number of interesting personalities from the past, including Oliver Cromwell. The ruins of the largest castle in England stand round the corner from Annie's and stones from here were included in the building of Windsor Castle.

Right in the centre of town, in a Grade II listed building that is over 300 years old, Jean Ann Rowlands gives a warm welcome to visitors from all over the world who come to taste her cakes, scones, pies and especially the home made teacakes which are served with home made jams.

The pink and burgundy room is a relaxing setting in which to enjoy your tea. The walls are decorated with old paintings and views of Wallingford and paintings by local customers are displayed for sale. On fine days, a small walled garden at the back allows 'alfresco' teas after you have explored the ancient highways of the town. *Teas served:* Indian, Earl Grey, Ceylon, Darjeeling, Traditional English Blend, Assam, Lapsang Souchong. *Fruit flavoured teas and herbal infusions are also offered.*

BIRD ON THE ROCK TEAROOM

Owners: Douglas & Annabel Hawkes

**Abcott, Clungunford
Shropshire SY7 0PX
Tel:/Fax: 01588 660631**

Directions
The tearoom is 8 miles from Ludlow and is situated on the B4367 between Craven Arms and Hoptonheath.

Opening times
Open all year.
Closed Mondays, except Bank Holidays.
Summer, Tuesday–Sunday, 10 am–6 pm.
Winter, Tuesday–Sunday, 10 am–5 pm.

Local Interest:
*Nearby Ludlow is a medieval wool town and Stokesay
Castle is an English Heritage Property. There is also
wonderful walking countryside at Offas Dyke and
Long Mynd.*

Cottage garden flowers and climbers create a memorable sight as you approach this pretty 17th century house. And inside the traditional Welsh longhouse with its oak beams and quarry tiles, Annabel and Douglas Hawkes have created a marvellous early 20th century atmosphere with 1920s, 30s and 40s music and memorabilia collected during their careers in the film industry. As costume designers for several period films and TV dramas (including Poirot, Pride and Prejudice and House of Elliot), the couple has a real flair for recreating the past. Both the interior and garden of this excellent, charming tearoom delight everyone who visits.

At tea-time, Miss Marple's Murderous Mixture allows you to choose 'something savoury, something sweet' with your pot of tea or coffee, while the Claude Greengrass Poacher's Tea of hot buttered crumpets and a slice of Mrs Beaton's half pound cake has a true old-fashioned appeal. In summer, the Hercule Poirot Sleuth Tea serves Poirot's favourite lemon tea with bread and jam and wonderful cakes. *Tea served:* Assam, Darjeeling, Nilgiri, Dimbula, Nuwara Eliya, Keemun, Yunnan, Russian Caravan, Rose Pouchong, Lapsang Souchong, Gunpowder, Chunmee, Formosa Oolong, Earl Grey, Lady Grey, Lemon, Old English Fruits, Spice Imperial, various own blends including a good strong Shropshire Blend of Assam, Kenya, Nuwara Eliya and Lapsang Souchong. *Herbal infusions are also offered.*

Benson's of Stratford-Upon-Avon

Owner: Max Lawrence

**4 Bards Walk, Stratford-upon-Avon
Warwickshire CV37 6EY
Tel: 01789 261116**

Directions

Benson's is off Henley Street, two minutes walk from Shakespeare's birthplace in the town centre.

Opening times

Open all year except Sundays in winter.
Monday–Friday, 10 am–5.30 pm.
Saturday, 8.30 am–5.30 pm.
Sunday (summer only), 10 am-4.30 pm.

Local Interest:

Benson's is right in the centre of Shakespeare's town. From the shop you can easily walk to Shakespeare's birthplace, his daughter, Judith's home and Holy Trinity Church where he is buried. Also close by is Harvard House, home of the man who set up Harvard University in the USA and a place of pilgrimage for Americans.

This very light and airy conservatory-style tea shop is in a refurbished Victorian arcade that was once Osbornes Court, a row of eight little cottages converted from a Malt House between 1809 and 1821. The display of the patisseries that fills the 19th century window of the shop will tempt you inside and you will find yourself in an extremely calm and relaxing interior that is bright with the colour of the plants and flowers around the room and the original watercolours on the walls.

Max Lawrence worked in Switzerland for a while and has a flair for serving mouthwatering pastries. The mille feuille with fresh fruit is too good to miss but if you prefer something savoury with your afternoon tea, the gourmet sandwiches with all sorts of possible fillings are absolutely wonderful. Try carved ham with cream cheese and melon or Stilton with apple, or make up your own combination. A set afternoon tea will give you smoked salmon sandwiches followed by home baked scones with jam and cream and a speciality tea served in one of the Shakespeare teapots, each of which represents a different Shakespeare play. *Teas served:* House Blend, Earl Grey, English Breakfast, Assam, Darjeeling, Ceylon, Lapsang Souchong, decaffeinated. *Herbal infusions are also offered.*

NORTH EAST
REGIONAL MAP

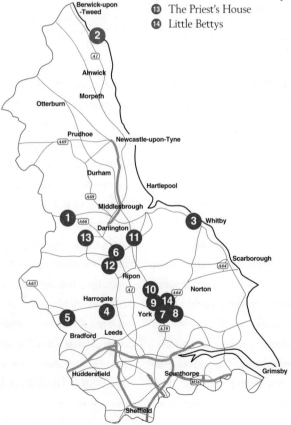

THE MARKET PLACE TEASHOP

Owner: Robert Hilton

29 Market Place, Barnard Castle
County Durham DL12 8NE
Tel: 01833 690110

Directions

The tea shop is in the centre of the cobbled Market Place.

Opening times

Open all year except two weeks at Christmas.
Monday–Saturday, 10 am–5.30 pm.
Sunday, 3–5.30 pm.

Awards

Egon Ronay recommended
Good Food Guide

Local Interest:

The town has interesting antique and craft shops in which to browse. On the outskirts, visit the Bowes Museum which has one of the finest art collections outside London, and Raby Castle, the seat of Lord Barnard. Drive to nearby High Force, the highest waterfall in England, and enjoy surrounding Teesdale countryside.

In the very heart of this attractive old market town, you will find the Market Place Teashop in an early 17th century building that long ago was a house before it became a pub and later a gentleman's outfitters selling typical country garments to local farm workers. The front of the tea shop was probably the original master's house, and servants quarters and stables were behind and alongside in Waterloo Yard. Today, the upstairs Artisan shop and picture gallery has a good selection of gifts, prints and original paintings.

The tea shop itself, which is celebrating its 29th anniversary this year, is a charming room full of character, with flagstones on the floor and an open stone fireplace. Tea is served in silver teapots by friendly waitresses in smart burgundy-striped uniforms and they will bring you whatever you choose from the tempting list of home-baked cakes that changes daily. Try the meringues filled with cream and strawberries, the strawberry tarts or the Yorkshire Curd Cheesecake. The high quality of all the food and the attractive, welcoming atmosphere make this an excellent place for lunch or afternoon tea. *Teas served:* Typhoo, Earl Grey, Ceylon, Traditional English, Assam, Darjeeling, Lapsang Souchong, China. *Fruit flavoured teas and herbal infusions are also offered.*

THE COPPER KETTLE TEA ROOMS

Owners: Pat and Heather Green

21 Front Street, Bamburgh
Northumberland NE69 7BW
Tel: 01668 214315

Directions
From the A1, take either the B1341 or the B1342 to Bamburgh. The Copper Kettle is in the heart of the village.

Opening times
Open from mid-February–end of November.
Mondays, closed.
Tuesdays–Sundays, 10.30 am–late afternoon.
Open all Bank Holidays.
Telephone to check opening times.

Local Interest:
Visit the Norman castle and the 13th century church where you will find the grave of Grace Darling, the heroine of the rescue of survivors from a wrecked steamer. The Grace Darling Museum houses more souvenirs.

After a tour of Bamborough Castle or a walk in the sea air, don't miss the opportunity of afternoon tea in the old-fashioned charm of the Copper Kettle 18th century tearoom or cottage patio. Outside, a bright display of colourful flowers at the front door and windows welcomes you, while inside your eye will be caught by the collection of gleaming copper kettles, old teapots and interesting knick-knacks which are all for sale. In summer the patio garden is a riot of colour and provides a sun trap where refreshments are served under the shade of large umbrellas.

Everything on the menu is home-made and the selection is extremely tempting. The traditional, open, and toasted sandwiches are filled with such treats as local crab, home cooked ham, or smoked salmon with dill pickle and cream cheese. These all come with freshly tossed salads or garnishes and the option of Pat's Pickle. The cakes and desserts are equally mouth-watering – lemon tea loaf, meringues, nut cake, moist apple cake, American style poppy seed muffins, pecan pie, tipsy tart with brandy, and cream teas with whipped cream. *Teas served:* Assam, Ceylon, China, Darjeeling, Earl Grey, Traditional English, Lapsang Souchong, Rose Pouchong, decaffeinated, organic. *Fruit flavoured teas and herbal infusions are also offered.*

ELIZABETH BOTHAM & SONS

Managing Director: Mike Jarman

35/39 Skinner Street
Whitby, North Yorkshire
YO21 3AH
Tel: 01947 602823
Fax: 01947 820269
Website: www.botham.co.uk
E-mail: MJ@botham.co.uk

Directions
Botham's is at the top of Skinner Street on the West Cliff. There is a car park nearby.

Opening times
Open all year except Sundays. September–May, Tuesday–Saturday, 9 am–4.30 pm. June, July, August, Monday–Saturday, 9 am–4.30 pm. Telephone to check opening times.

Local Interest:
Whitby is an old-fashioned fishing town in the heart of the North Yorkshire country park so enjoys the beauties of open moorland, the north sea, unspoilt beaches and the impressive ruins of Whitby Abbey on the East Cliff. The local museum tells the story of Captain Cook's travels and other seafaring adventures.

In 1865, Elizabeth Botham established a bakery in Whitby and today, Sarah, her great granddaughter is carrying on the tradition with her husband, Mike Jarman and her two brothers, Jo and Nick. And not only does the company continue to make the same biscuits, breads, cakes and pastries as the Victorian shop was famous for, they have expanded the business and now have a restaurant and cafe (originally set up in the 1920s), celebration cake and hamper service as well as the retail shop and mail order/website options for those who can't get to Yorkshire to taste or buy.

To get to the restaurant on the first floor, you have to walk past the truly mouth-watering array of cakes and confectionery. If you manage to drag yourself away from the display and climb the stairs, you will find yourself in a welcoming comfortable room where waiting staff in reassuring black and white are attentive and helpfully friendly. The menu includes plenty of traditional English dishes for indulgent breakfasts, satisfying lunches and excellent teas, any of which may be enjoyed with a pot of fine loose leaf tea. *Teas served:* Botham's Special Blend Resolution Tea (5p from each retail pack sold goes to the rebuilding of Captain Cook's famous ship, the Resolution: this is the only Botham's tea packed in teabags), Ceylong Orange Pekoe, Darjeeling, English Breakfast, Earl Grey, Gunpowder, Jasmine, Lapsang Souchong.

BETTYS CAFÉ TEA ROOMS

Manager: Nick Carroll

1 Parliament Street, Harrogate
North Yorkshire HG1 2QU
Tel: 01423 502746   Fax: 01423 565191
Website: www.bettysbypost.com

Directions
Bettys is located on the main route through the centre of Harrogate from Leeds to Ripon, opposite the War Memorial and overlooking Montpellier Gardens.

Opening times
Open all year.
Monday–Sunday, 9 am–9 pm.

Awards
1990, 91, 92, 93 & 96 Tea Council Award of Excellence
1994 Tea Council Top Tea Place of The Year
Egon Ronay recommended

Local Interest:
Wander around Harrogate's wide selection of interesting shops, or walk through Valley Gardens and Harlow Carr Botanical Gardens. Three miles away in Knaresborough, see the oldest chemist's shop in England and visit Mother Shipton's Cave, the home of a 15th century prophet.

The Harrogate branch of Bettys was the first tearoom opened by Frederick Belmont in 1919. The young confectioner arrived from Switzerland and settled in North Yorkshire where he found the clear air very much to his liking. His natural talent for creating exceptionally good cakes and his Swiss flair for hospitality were the perfect combination to build a thriving business and very soon he opened more shops in other Yorkshire towns. Today, the company is still owned by direct descendents of Frederick's family, now half Swiss, half Yorkshire, but still no-one knows the identity of Betty!

Frederick Belmont's guiding principle

was, "If we want things just right, we have to make them ourselves" and today, Bettys Bakery still makes all the cakes, pastries, chocolates, breads, rolls, fruit loaves, scones and muffins, and all dishes on the menu are freshly prepared on the premises.

Teas and coffees are specially imported and blended by Bettys sister company, Taylors of Harrogate. A café pianist plays every evening from 6 pm to 9 pm. *Teas served:* Tea Room Blend, Special Estate Darjeeling, Special Estate Tippy Assam, Earl Grey, Lapsang Souchong, Yunnan Flowery Orange Pekoe, China Gui Hua, Mountains of the Moon, Zulu, iced tea in summer. *Fruit flavoured teas and herbal infusions are also offered.*

BETTYS CAFÉ TEA ROOMS

Manager: Sally Carter

**32–34 The Grove, Ilkley
West Yorkshire LS29 9EE
Tel: 01943 608029   Fax: 01943 816723
Website: www.bettysbypost.com**

Directions
Bettys is in Ilkley town centre, backing on to
the main Pay and Display car park and not far
from the station and tourist information centre.

Opening times
Open all year.
Monday–Sunday, 9 am–6 pm.

Awards
1990, 91, 92 & 96 Tea Council Award of Excellence
1993 Tea Council Top Tea Place of The Year
Egon Ronay recommended

Local Interest:
*Visit the Victorian Arcade, the Manor House Museum, the
Kings Hall and Winter Gardens and drive or walk out of
town across Ilkley Moor to see some of Yorkshire's most
impressive countryside.*

This is one of the five hugely successful Bettys Café Tea Rooms in Yorkshire and the special feature of this branch is the wonderful, colourful collection of over 200 teapots that are arranged on a high shelf that runs all round the tearoom. Recently refurbished, Bettys in Ilkley boasts a striking wrought iron canopy and extensive tea and coffee counter, stacked with antique tea caddies. The tearoom has some specially commissioned stained glass windows that depict some of the wild flowers found on the Yorkshire moors, and 'La Chasse', the largest marquetry picture ever made in the Spindler studio, which shows a medieval hunting scene.

This is a haven for ramblers who reach the town tired and in need of refreshment after walking for miles across the rugged, wind-swept moorland. They and other visitors can relax and enjoy the fabulous selection of pastries, breads and cakes that arrive fresh from Bettys Bakery every day. To add to the attraction, a pianist plays every Thursday and Sunday lunchtime and from 4.30–6 pm on Fridays and Saturdays. *Teas served:* Tea Room Blend, Special Estate Darjeeling, Special Estate Tippy Assam, Earl Grey, Lapsang Souchong, Yunnan Flowery Orange Pekoe, China Gui Hua, Mountains of the Moon, Zulu, iced tea (a blend of Earl Grey and Ceylon) in summer. *Fruit flavoured teas and herbal infusions are also offered.*

Bettys Café Tea Rooms

Manager: Lindsay Judd

188 High Street, Northallerton
North Yorkshire DL7 8LF
Tel: 01609 775154 Fax: 01609 777552
Website: www.bettysbypost.com

Directions
Bettys is situated in the town centre, in the main shopping street.

Opening times
Open all year. Monday–Saturday,
9 am–5.30 pm. Sunday, 10 am–5.30 pm.

Awards
1987   Tea Council Top Tea Place of The Year
1990   Tea Council Award of Excellence
Egon Ronay recommended

Local Interest:
The town has a market every Wednesday and some interesting shops. It is a good centre for walking and is five miles from Old Motherley, one of the best walks in the area.

This is the northerly of the five branches of Bettys and it is a real treasure, tucked away in the Saxon market town of Northallerton. It is said that Roman soldiers once marched along the Great North Road that passes very close by and the town is mentioned in the Domesday Book, so there is lots of history here. It was in this delightful setting that Bettys opened the most recent addition to their chain of fantastic Yorkshire tea shops. The company is still owned by the family of the founder, Frederick Belmont, and teas and coffees are specially blended for the shops by the sister company, Taylors of Harrogate.

The sunny golden room here in Northallerton is small and intimate and decorated with Art Deco mirrors and antique teapots. As you step inside the red brick Georgian building, your attention will be caught by the selection of wonderful cakes and pastries that fill the counter. How does one ever decide what to eat? There are just so many delicious things to try. More than one visit is recommended in order to work your way through at least some of the selection. *Teas served:* Tea Room Blend, Special Estate Darjeeling, Special Estate Tippy Assam, Earl Grey, Lapsang Souchong, Yunnan Flowery Orange Pekoe, China Gui Hua, Mountains of the Moon, Zulu. *Fruit flavoured teas and herbal infusions are also offered.*

Bettys Café Tea Rooms

Manager: Paula Bissett

6–8 St Helen's Square, York
North Yorkshire YO1 2QP
Tel: 01904 659142 Fax: 01904 627050
Website: www.bettysbypost.com

Directions
Bettys is located in the city centre, just round the corner from York Minster.

Opening times
Open all year.
Monday–Sunday, 9 am–9 pm.

Awards
Egon Ronay recommended
1997 Tea Council Award of Excellence

Local Interest:
From Bettys you can walk to the Minster, The Treasurer's House, Merchant Taylors' Hall, Yorkshire Museum and Museum Gardens, St Mary's Abbey, the Railway War Memorial, Waxworks, open air market and lots more.

This 'continental style' tearoom is set in the heart of York, and from the huge picture windows that dominate the ground floor tearoom, you can look out over the cobbled streets of this historical city. The elegant surroundings were inspired by the interior of the luxury liner, the Queen Mary. Frederick Belmont, Bettys' founder, travelled on the maiden voyage of this ocean liner in 1936, during which time he dreamt up the plans for a new flagship café in York. The liner's interior decorators were commissioned to design the new tearoom, recreating the magnificent panelling, pillars and mirrors that had adorned the Queen Mary. Many of the original 1930s features have recently been refurbished and the Belmont Room, on the first floor, has reopened after many years for group bookings and private parties.

The cakes and pastries are still made daily by hand at Bettys Craft Bakery, just as they were back in the 1930s. Today, an added attraction is the Cafe Pianist who plays every evening from 6 pm to 9 pm. *Teas served:* Tea Room Blend, Special Estate Darjeeling, Special Estate Tippy Assam, Earl Grey, Lapsang Souchong, Yunnan Flowery Orange Pekoe, China Gui Hua, Mountains of the Moon, Zulu. *Fruit flavoured teas and herbal infusions are also available.*

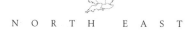

BULLIVANT OF YORK

Owner: Christine Bullivant

15 Blake Street
York YO1 2QJ
Tel: 01904 671311

Directions
From York Minster, walk along Duncombe

Place to the cross roads. Turn left into Blake Street and the tea shop is about 150 yards along.

Opening times
Open seven days a week.
Please telephone for details.

Local Interest:
The tea shop is near all of York's main attractions – the Minster, St Mary's Abbey, York Castle, Yorkshire Museum and Museum Gardens.

Christine Bullivant's main concern is that her customers should feel pampered and relaxed in her charming, intimate tearoom and she is almost always on duty to welcome you. Her smiling and efficient staff will do their very best to make your visit a memorable one. The pretty pink decor, the pink Lloyd Loom chairs and the tables dressed in the Victorian breakfast table style make it a very special place to stop at any time of the day. A peaceful courtyard at the rear provides more seating in good weather and here you can sit surrounded by tubs full of flowers and climbing plants. Table reservations can be made.

Bullivant's menu offers an incredible range of sandwiches, club sandwiches, luncheons of wonderful cheeses, pies, pâtés, savoury pancakes and roast meats, and at tea time all the traditional favourites are on offer – cinnamon toast, Cream Teas with delicious home made scones with Cornish clotted cream and home made preserves, toasted teacakes, hot buttered crumpets and a really special rich dark fruit cake that is served with Wensleydale cheese.

The shop also has an enormous range of superb Collectors' Teapots and if you are interested, Christine's helpful staff will bring items of interest to your table so that you can choose in comfort what to buy to take home with you. *Teas served include:* Select Blend, Traditional English, Earl Grey, Ceylon, Lapsang Souchong, Rose Pouchong, China, Lemon. *Fruit flavoured teas and herbal infusions are also available.*

CLARK'S OF EASINGWOLD

Owners: Judy and Gerald Clark

195 Long Street
Easingwold
York YO6 3JB
Tel: 01347 821285

Directions
Easingwold is situated equidistant between York and Thirsk and is by-passed by the A19.

Clark's is the first building on the left as you turn into the main street from the York direction. Parking is at the rear or on the road outside.

Opening times
Open all year.
Monday–Saturday, 8.30 am–4 pm (in winter), or 5 pm (in summer).

Local Interest:
Now that Easingwold has been by-passed by the A19, it is a pleasant small town in which to browse on the way to the North Yorkshire Moors or Herriot Country.

Clark's was established in 1928 by Judy Clark's grandmother-in-law who served tea and home made scones to local cyclists from the kitchen window. She developed this promising business into a bakery, and built a wooden hut in the garden to serve as a café. This was used for many years until it was eventually demolished and replaced by the present café that was set up within the bakery shop in 1995. Now that the by-pass has eased the pressure of traffic on Easingwold, this is an extremely pleasant place to shop and browse.

Both Judy and Gerald are narrow boat enthusiasts and so have decorated the café with all sorts of canal wares to create an attractive interior – plates, pictures, posters and tea towels are displayed on shelves and on the trellis, and there is an old milk churn decorated in the style of narrow boat Buckby Ware. In good weather, there are chairs and tables in the pretty garden at the back.

The menu offers sandwiches, pies, pasties, ploughmans, soup, salads, and omelettes. Tea time brings teacakes, scones with jam and cream, cakes and pastries, and a set tea with a selection of savouries and sandwiches, scones and cakes. Everything is made on the premises and there is a wide choice of confectionery for sale in the bakery shop. *Teas served:* Yorkshire Blend, Earl Grey.

CLARK'S TEAROOMS

Owners: Judy and Gerald Clark

**Market Place, Easingwold
Yorkshire YO6 3AG
Tel: 01347 823143**

Directions
Easingwold, now by-passed by A19, is 13 miles north of York and ten miles south of Thirsk.

Clark's Tearooms is situated in the market square.

Opening times
Open all year except Sundays.
Monday, Tuesday, Wednesday, 10 am–5 pm.
Thursday and Saturday, 9.30 am–5 pm.
Friday, 9 am–5 pm.

Local Interest:
Easingwold is in the Vale of York and close to the North Yorkshire Moors and so is a good centre for walking and cycling.

All the breads, pastries and cakes served and sold at Clark's Tearooms are made at the shop's bakery that was set up 70 years ago and now houses Judy and Gerald's other tearoom and bakery shop about three quarters of a mile away on the edge of town. This main branch of the business here in the central Market Place is in the perfect location for shoppers and tourists, for either lunch or a refreshing pot of tea and one of the wonderful home made cakes. The pretty pink and green shop is divided into three rooms with a smokers' parlour at the back. Local artists display their paintings on the walls, and traditional dark furniture is set off by rose-printed curtains and tablecloths.

The menu includes sandwiches, home-baked savouries, breads and cakes, and local specialities such as Wensleydale cheese, Yorkshire fruit cake, Yorkshire curd tarts, and delicious fruit pies with cream. If you would like to buy some of these to take home, the Clarks have a bakery shop on the other side of the street which sells their breads, pastries and cakes. *Teas served:* House Blend, Darjeeling, Earl Grey. *Fruit flavoured teas and herbal infusions are also offered.*

CRATHORNE HALL HOTEL

General Manager: Mark Booth

**Crathorne Hall Hotel
Crathorne, Near Yarm
North Yorkshire TS15 0AR
Tel: 01642 700398**

Directions
Crathorne Hall is close to the A19 trunk road at Crathorne Village. From the south, take the slip road marked for A67 Yarm, Teeside

Airport and Kirklevington. From the north, take slip road A67 to Crathorne Village.

Opening times
Open all year. 7 am–10.30 pm every day.

Awards
1997 & 98 The Tea Council Award of Excellence

Local Interest:
There are castles (Richmond, Barnard, Middleham, Pickering), museums (Bowes, Beamish, The Jorvik Viking Museum), stately homes (Castle Howard, Ormesby Hall, Fairfax House), ruins (Rivaulx, Easby, Kirkham, Byland), Yorkshire Steam railway, racing (Ripon, Thirsk, York), Flamingo Land Zoo and Park, and beautiful Yorkshire coastline and beaches.

Crathorne Hall is one of Britain's finest Edwardian houses, built in 1906 and set in 15 acres of fine wooded grounds between the Yorkshire Dales and the North Yorkshire Moors. Many of the original features remain intact, including large stone fireplaces, ornate ceilings, wooden panelling and generous bay windows. The Drawing Room, the venue for Yorkshire Cream Teas and Afternoon Tea, boasts some very fine paintings, windows that open on to the spacious lawns where croquet is played in summer, and offers the welcome of roaring log fires in winter. The hotel's gastronomic team has created an impressive range of menus for different occasions, including the Grandma Gallagher selection of traditional desserts, which comes from recipes handed down from generation to generation. The hotel also runs Speciality Break weekends – three on offer are wine appreciation, petits fours skills, and murder mystery weekends! But if it's just tea you want, you will not be disappointed. This is a wonderful, elegant, relaxing location and really is perfect for stylish teas. *Teas served:* Breakfast Blend, China, Darjeeling, Indian, Earl Grey. *Various fruit flavoured teas and herbal infusions are also available.*

THE MAD HATTER TEA SHOP

Owners: Andrew Atkinson and
Stirling Jebb

**Market Place, Masham
Near Ripon, North Yorkshire
HG4 4EA
Tel: 01765 689129**

Directions

Masham is 20 miles north of Harrogate on the
A61 between Glasshouses and Jervaulx and

8 miles west off the A1 of the B6267. The tea shop
is in the heart of the town in the market square.

Opening times
Open all year* except Thursday.
Open 10 am–5 pm except Sunday, 11 am–5 pm.
* November through March also closed Monday.

Local Interest:
*Masham's two breweries, both nationally famous, draw
thousands of visitors each year. Set in gentle country at the
meeting of Wenslydale and Colsterdale, Masham is an ideal
starting point for relaxing country walks. There is a market in
the Old Market Square Wednesdays and Saturdays.*

The Mad Hatters is a Grade II listed
building dating from the 1830s and overlooks the huge four square Market Place
in Masham. The two tearooms are decorated in a traditional style and there is a
growing collection of plates, teapots and
pictures which all help create a homely
environment.

The menu includes plenty of
healthy options. The philosophy at the
Mad Hatter is to use only the freshest
of ingredients to produce a wide range
of meals. The most popular dishes
include filled French style baguettes
(baked fresh each morning on the
premises), open sandwiches, crispy
salad bowls (all with a wide range of
fillings/toppings) and Welsh rarebit
with bacon.

The range of cakes proves to be an
ever popular reason for customers
returning to the Mad Hatter Tea Shop.
The choice varies, but the favourites
include: baked lemon cheesecake, apple
and cinnamon and orange marmalade.
The home made scones with a hint of
nutmeg always go down well.

The Mad Hatter also sells a range of
hand made jams and speciality teas and
coffees. *Teas served:* Assam, Ceylon,
Darjeeling, China, Earl Grey, English
Breakfast, Formosa Lapsang Souchong,
Yorkshire. *Fruit flavoured teas and herbal
teas are also available.*

THE PRIEST'S HOUSE

Owners: Robert Hodgson and
Jo Parkinson

**Barden, Near Skipton
North Yorkshire BD23 6AS
Tel: 01756 720616**

Directions
From Leeds, take the A65 to Addingham.
Follow directions to Bolton Abbey. Take the
B6160 to Burnsall. Barden is between Bolton

Abbey and Burnsall, approximately 3 miles
from Bolton Abbey. You will see the ruins of
Barden Tower on the right. The gateway is
signposted.

Opening times
Open mid-March–end October, 10.30 am–5 pm.
Closed Thursday and Friday. Please ring to
confirm winter opening times.

Local Interest:
*Bolton Abbey is 3 miles away. Lovely riverside and
moorland walks. Strid Wood (Special Site of Scientific
Interest SSSI) is a mile away.*

The tearooms lie in the heart of the beautiful Yorkshire Dales, located in a 15th century building next to the ruins of Barden Tower. Since establishing the business here in 1991, Robert and Jo have built up a regular trade with summer visitors to the area.

You can take tea either outside overlooking the ruins or inside in the Oak room – so called because of its oak beamed ceiling and magnificent oak dressers which house a fine collection of antique Willow Pattern meat platters (echoed in the crockery used in the tearoom). Many people comment on the wonderfully relaxed atmosphere of the Oak Room with its historic features

and gentle period background music.

Light refreshments are served throughout the day. Afternoon Tea is always popular, both in summer when sultana and lemon scones with jam and cream are a particular favourite, and in winter months when customers prefer toasted crumpets or fruit loaf by the log fire.

The water from the shop's moorland spring makes fantastic tea and some customers even bring bottles to fill so that they can take some away to enjoy at home. *Teas served:* Traditional Blend, Assam, Darjeeling, Earl Grey, Lapsang Souchong, Sri Lanka Golden. *Herbal infusions are also available.*

LITTLE BETTYS

Manager: Janet Parker

46 Stonegate, York
North Yorkshire, YO1 2AS
Tel: 01904 622865
Fax: 01904 640348
Website: www.bettysbypost.com

Directions
Taylors is very close to York Minster in Petergate.

Opening times
Open all year. Monday–Sunday, 9 am–5.30 pm.

Awards
1991, 92 & 93 Tea Council Award of Excellence
Egon Ronay recommended

Local Interest:
Within walking distance of the tearoom are York Minster,
The Treasurer's House, the Merchant Taylors' Hall, St Mary's
Abbey, Yorkshire Museum and Museum Gardens, Waxworks,
York Castle and Museum, Cliffords Tower, Coppergate
Shopping Centre and so much more.

There's a second Bettys Café Tea Rooms in York – the adorably named 'Little Bettys' situated in a Grade II listed building in medieval Stonegate, just a stone's throw from York Minster.

Little Bettys, just as the name implies, is the smallest of the Bettys Café Tea Rooms. In the Café, situated up a flight of winding stairs, the roaring fires, wooden beams and beautiful interior are almost as much a source of refreshment as the tea itself. As with all the Bettys Café Tea Rooms, there's an outstanding selection of teas and coffees, chocolates, breads, cakes and Yorkshire specialities such as Fat Rascals, spiced Yorkshire Teacakes and Yorkshire Curd Tarts.

The downstairs shop is the perfect place to buy freshly made cappuccinos, espressos and cups of fine teas, along with sandwiches and cakes to take away for a picnic by the River Ouse.

Once you have tried and become addicted to the excellent foods and teas you can have a regular supply sent by post by telephoning Harrogate 01423 886055. *Teas served:* Yorkshire Gold Blend, Choice Assam, Special Estate Tippy Assam, Fine Darjeeling BOP, Vintage Darjeeling, Fine Ceylon BOP, Ceylon Orange Pekoe, Earl Grey, Keemun, Lapsang Souchong, Mountains of the Moon, China Gui Hua, Japanese Cherry, Zulu. *Fruit flavoured teas and herbal infusions are also offered.*

N O R T H   W E S T
R E G I O N A L   M A P

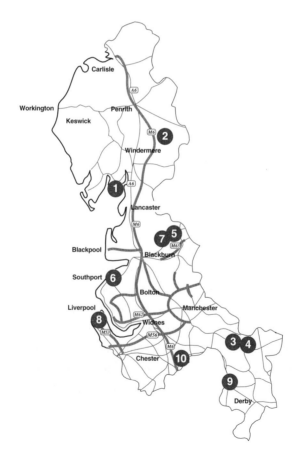

HAZELMERE CAFE & BAKERY

Owners: Dorothy and Ian Stubley

1 Yewbarrow Terrace
Grange over Sands
Cumbria LA11 6ED
Tel: 015395 32972
Fax: 015395 34101

Directions
When coming into Grange over Sands on the B5277, you will pass Grange station on the left. Shortly after this, there is a mini-roundabout. Take the first exit and the Cafe is about 25 yards along, on the right.

Opening times
Open all year. 10 am–4.30 pm in winter, 10 am–5 pm in summer.

Awards
1998 Tea Council Award of Excellence

Local Interest:
The Hazelmere overlooks Grange's famous ornamental gardens. The bay is a perfect place for walks on the sand and a short ride by car will take you up into the Lake District.

Grange over Sands is one of those towns that just would not be complete without a high-class tea shop, and the Hazelmere, set in a parade of Victorian shops fronted by a beautiful ornate glass and cast iron verandah provides the perfect venue for tea, and also manages to recapture the spirit of traditional tea time. Dorothy and Ian Stubley specialise in home made quality food using only the best ingredients, including free-range eggs and fresh cream. They make everything on the premises and like to include a mixture of local specialities as well as their own original recipes.

You can be absolutely sure that you will not be disappointed by the selection of real treats – Cumberland rum nicky, Yorkshire curd tart, date and walnut fudge tart, a variety of home made scones with Plum jam and Lakeland cream, and sandwiches filled with Cheddar cheese and home made piccalilli or oak roasted salmon with horseradish or turkey breast and apple sauce. Light meals are also available. *Teas served:* House Blend (Brunswick Estate B.O.P. Ceylon), 3 Japanese, 6 Single Estate Ceylon, Single Estate Indonesian, 4 China, 2 Single Estate Indian and different guest teas. *Fruit flavoured teas and herbal infusions are also available.*

NEW VILLAGE TEA ROOMS

Owner: Christine Evans

Orton, Penrith
Cumbria CA10 3RH
Tel: 015396 24886

Directions
Leave the M6 at junction 38 and take the Appleby road. In Orton, take the Shap road in front of the George Hotel. The tearooms are straight ahead, opposite the stores and Post Office, where the road turns left and leaves the village.

Opening times
Open all year.
July–August, 10 am–6 pm. April, May, June, September, October, 10 am–5 pm.
November, March, 10.30 am–4.30 pm.

Local Interest:
Orton is an interesting village with buildings dating back to the 17th and 18th centuries. It is an ideal centre for visits to the Lake District, the Yorkshire Dales, the North Pennines, the Border Country and Morecambe Bay. The Wainwright 'Coast to Coast' walk (from St Bees to Robin Hood's Bay) touches the village.

The New Village Tea Rooms are housed in an 18th century building which has had a varied history and was most recently a cottage. The downstairs tearoom was once the cottage living room and the kitchen is open to the friendly area where customers now sit to enjoy their tea. This means that they can chat to the staff while their food is being prepared and feel really at home.

On hot summer days, the tearooms remain cool and comfortable but sunlovers can bask outside in the pretty cottage garden. In winter, an open coal fire keeps visitors warm and cosy and creates a haven for walkers. Californian 'Coast to Coast' walkers who visited when walking west to east in 1992 and again when walking east to west in 1994, said that the sticky toffee pudding was the best in the country and took the recipe home, vowing to keep it a secret forever.

All the food is prepared on the premises using traditional methods and locally produced quality ingredients. The menu offers a wide range of home made cakes, tempting desserts, sandwiches and hot lunch dishes in a totally smoke-free environment. *Teas served:* Earl Grey, Ceylon, Darjeeling, Assam, Lapsang Souchong, PG Tips. *Fruit flavoured teas and herbal infusions are also offered.*

THE COTTAGE TEA ROOM

Owners: Bill and Betty Watkins

3 Fennel Street, Ashford-in-the-Water
Near Bakewell, Derbyshire DE45 1QF
Tel: 01629 812488

Directions
Ashford-in-the-Water lies on the A6, two miles
north of Bakewell and eight miles south of
Buxton Spa. The tearoom is just above the ford
by the ancient sheepwash bridge.

Opening times
Open all the year except one week in
mid-September, Christmas Day, Boxing Day
and New Year's Day. Monday, Wednesday,
Thursday, Saturday and Sunday teas are
served 2.30–5 pm. Closed Tuesday and
Friday afternoons.

Award
Egon Ronay recommended
1998 Tea Council Award of Excellence

Local Interest:
*Ashford-in-the-Water, once part of the Duke of Devon-
shire's Chatsworth Estate, is considered to be the jewel of
The Peak District National Park. Five bridges span the
River Wye (famous amongst anglers). The Norman church
contains examples of the local coloured marble and there
is a carefully restored 14th century tithe barn.*

You take a step back in time when you find the charming Cottage Tea Room in this unspoilt village on the old Drovers Road from Inverness to London. Here, journeymen and visitors have paused for refreshment for many a day, long before the Peak District became the nation's first National Park.

The unchanging quality is the treasured feature of Betty and Bill Watkins' tearoom where customers are served at lace-covered tables with freshly brewed leaf tea and dainty bakery as were their grandparents in earlier decades. Open throughout the year, a friendly welcome awaits you on sun-drenched summer days and on snowy winter ones when tea by an open fire is especially tempting.

The accent is on genuine home cooking. There is a wonderful array of traditional English cakes and hand-kneaded breads, and a variety of feather-light scones is baked daily. The warm cheesy herb scones are a great favourite on winter days. Six set meals are served and you can choose anything from a simple pot of tea and a slice of cake to the full afternoon tea. *Teas served:* In addition to the specially blended House tea, an extensive selection of leaf teas is available, including 6 China, 5 Ceylon, 3 Indian, Kenya, Formosa Oolong, Russian Caravan, Earl Grey and English Breakfast. *A range of herbal infusions is also provided.*

NORTHERN TEA MERCHANTS

Owner: David Pogson

Crown House
193 Chatsworth Road, Brampton
Chesterfield, Derbyshire S40 2BA
Tel: 01246 233243
Fax: 01246 555991

Directions

Northern Tea Merchants is situated one mile

from the centre of Chesterfield on the A619 (the road to Chatsworth House).

Opening times
Open all year except Bank Holidays, for a week from Christmas to New Year, and Sundays. Monday–Friday, 9 am–5 pm.
Saturday, 9 am–4.30 pm. Sunday, closed.

Local Interest:
Chesterfield's crooked spire on the Church of St Mary and All Saints is a famous tourist attraction, and don't miss the interior of the church, the market place and conservation area with its early 16th century timber-framed inn.

The windows of Northern Tea Merchants' double-fronted store, not far from the famous crooked spire, are full of eye-catching tea and coffee equipment – scales, caddies, grinders, tea chests, tea wares and attractive packages. The family business, dating back to 1936, specialises in tea blending and packing and the manufacture of tea bags (as well as coffee roasting, grinding and packaging), and handles enough for 100 million cups a year. Proprietor David Pogson is recognised as an authority on tea and acts as a judge in Tea Council tea-tasting competitions. His shop is an absolute treasure trove of speciality teas, coffees and equipment, and shelves are stacked

high with an incredible choice of packages. This is a place of serious tea drinking where you can sample some of the unusual varieties at the tea bar before selecting your purchases from a range of 24 blends and single source teas. Visitors can also choose from a mouthwatering selection of scones, cakes and pastries to accompany their tea. Teas served: Golden De Luxe Classic, Silver De Luxe, Rwanda, Guangxi Guihua, Darjeeling, Assam, Ceylon, Ceylon Orange Pekoe, Keemun, Lapsang Souchong, Earl Grey, English Breakfast, Kenya, Russian Caravan, Formosa Oolong, Gunpowder, Jasmine. Fruit flavoured teas and herbal infusions are also available.

CAFÉ CAPRICE

Owners: Peter and Joyce Jenkinson

6 Moor Lane
Clitheroe
Lancashire BB7 1BE
Tel: 01200 422034

Directions
Leave the A49 at the Clitheroe turn off.
On entering the town centre, Café Caprice
is on the left.

Opening times
Open all year.
Monday, Tuesday, Thursday, Friday,
Saturday, 9.30 am–4.30 pm.
Wednesday and Sunday, closed.

Local Interest:
*Clitheroe has a castle with a Norman keep and a good
museum, the library is housed in an interesting building
dating back to 1800, and the Tourist Information Centre
organises walks through the town that give you all the
history.*

Café Caprice has a brand new image and menu. The neutral shades have gone and instead, the colour scheme is vibrant, lively, bright colours – strong blues and yellows on the walls and tablecloths in salmon and green, yellow and blue. And pictures on the wall and the bright blue and yellow outfits worn by the waiting staff add more splashes of similar colours to create a cheerful, friendly, happy atmosphere. But the modern look doesn't mean that the old-fasioned friendliness and service have gone. They are still very much in evidence, as are Joyce Jenkinson's talents in the kitchen and interest in food and traditional cookery. There is now a book room in the shop where you can browse through and buy all sorts of books on cookery, food and drink.

The menu features an excellent range of cakes including Cumbrian lemon loaf, carrot cake, chocolate cake, orange Victoria sandwich and lime and coconut slice. And all the favourite traditionals are on offer as well – crumpets, toasted teacakes, cream teas with oven-fresh scones, all sorts of sandwiches. *Teas served:* House Blend, Ceylon, Assam, Darjeeling, Earl Grey, Formosa Oolong, Lemon.

NOSTALGIA TEAROOMS

Owner: Ann Couzens

**215–217 Lord Street, Southport
Lancashire PR8 1NZ
Tel: 01704 501294**

Directions
Nostalgia is opposite the Tourist Information Centre, on the first floor of the black and white building, above The Early Learning Centre.

Opening times
Open all year. Monday, open only in July and August, 9.30 am–5 pm.
Tuesday–Saturday, 9.30 am–5 pm.
Sunday, 10 am–5 pm.

Local Interest:
Southport has a steam locomotive museum, the Atkinson Art Gallery, Warfarers Arcade with its statue of Red Rum and Marine Lake with fun fair, boating, walks and a miniature railway.

Ann Couzens had already enjoyed considerable success with her first tearoom in Birkdale before opening this Southport branch in one of the town's typical Victorian arcades. Ann used to be a catering teacher in one of the local schools and several of her staff are past pupils whom she has trained individually in the traditional preparation, presentation and service of food and in customer relations. She also designed the furniture and the interior decoration herself so that the large airy room would look absolutely right. Styled on a conservatory, with bamboo chairs and a colour scheme in pale pink and green, this is an elegant and restful place to take tea, where waitresses in pretty Victorian black and white costumes look after you in the old-fashioned way.

The generous menu which is supplemented by a daily blackboard, includes modern as well as traditional cakes – the Pavlova and Choux gateau are extremely tempting. And there are ice cream sundaes with exotic names such as Mississippi Steamboat and Singapore Surprise. But, even if you settle for just a cup of tea and a flapjack, you are bound to enjoy the reassuring Englishness of the experience. *Teas served:* Yorkshire Gold Premium, English Breakfast, Earl Grey, Darjeeling, Ceylon, Assam. *Fruit flavoured teas and herbal infusions are also offered.*

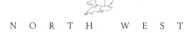

THE TOBY JUG TEA SHOP

Owners: Peter, Marie and Jane Ireland

20 King Street, Whalley
Clitheroe, Lancashire
BB7 9SL
Tel: 01254 823298
Fax: 01254 823298

Directions
The Toby Jug is in the main street of Whalley Village, by the bridge over the River Calder.

Opening times
Open all year except Sundays and Mondays.
Open Tuesday–Friday, 10 am–4.30 pm, Saturday, 10.30 am–5 pm.

Local Interest:
Whalley is an attractive village with some good shops and a parish church that has some interesting Saxon crosses in the churchyard. The Cistercian Abbey is mostly in ruins but the Chapter House is still used as a retreat.

The Toby Jug Tea Shop, originally King Street Farm and now a Grade II listed building, in days gone by, would have provided a welcome resting place for weary pilgrims on their way to the mother church in Whalley, which dates back to 1206 and today houses the beautiful 15th century choir stalls taken from the Cistercian Abbey nearby. In the churchyard are three Celtic preaching crosses. The village, in the heart of the Ribble Valley, nestles beneath Pendle Hill, where the Quaker founder, George Fox, preached in 1652, and which is closely associated with the infamous Pendle witches and their subsequent trial and hanging in Lancaster in 1612.

The Toby Jug, the Ireland's family home, offers traditional Lancashire hospitality and creates a cosy atmosphere with its oak beams and panelling plundered from the Abbey. The menu is packed with delicious lunchtime savouries and sandwich ideas, and for tea there are scones and an extensive range of tempting cakes, gateaux and fruit pies, all made on the premises and so reminiscent of days gone by. *Teas served:* Yorkshire Blend, Assam, Earl Grey, Darjeeling, English Breakfast, Lapsang Souchong, Jasmine Blossom, Orange and Lemon, decaffeinated. *Peppermint infusion is also available.*

LE PREMIER ETAGE

Managers: Rod and Brian Heron

42 Hamilton Square
Birkenhead, Merseyside L41 5BP
Tel: 0151 647 8095
Fax: 0151 647 6466

Directions
Follow signs for the city centre and park in one
of the town's car parks. Walk to Hamilton

Square Gardens right in the centre. Le
Premier Etage is on the south west side of the
square. Parking also available in the square.

Opening times
Open all year.
Sunday and Monday, closed.
Tuesday–Friday, 11 am–4 pm.
Saturday, 12 noon–4 pm.

Local Interest:
Birkenhead has an old heritage tramway, two museums,
Birkenhead Priory and Hamilton Square with its largest
group of Grade I listed Georgian buildings in Britain.

Le Premier Etage is on the first floor of an elegant and spacious Grade I listed Georgian building that has stunning views over Hamilton Square Gardens. The tearoom provides a relaxed and friendly atmosphere that appeals to locals and tourists alike, and for business people in a hurry, the restaurant offers an "executive fax service" that allows you to order ahead. With its red leather Chesterfield style sofas and cane backed chairs, the decor is traditional and attractive, and the high quality of the food and service make lunch or afternoon tea a special occasion.

The wide selection of modern English style cuisine offers anything from a light healthy mouthful to a mini feast. Crois-sants and sandwiches are filled with imaginative mixtures such as smoked bacon and melted brie, smoked salmon with lemon and horseradish cream, prawn with apple and celery; from the grill there are crumpets, teacakes, potato cakes and walnut bread; and the dessert selection includes white chocolate trifle, classic lemon tart and a range of tea breads. Afternoon Tea, served from 2 pm until 4 pm, includes mixed sandwiches, fresh scones and a selection of cakes to finish. *Teas served*: House Blend, First Flush Darjeeling, Assam Nahorhabi, Ceylon Dotel Oya, Hubei Silver Strawberries, Jasmine Chung Hao, Silver Tip Oolong, Earl Grey, Fuchow Golden Monkey.

GREYSTONES 17TH CENTURY TEA ROOM

Owners: Roger and Janet Warrillow

Stockwell Street
Leek, Staffs, ST13 6DH
Tel:/Fax: 01538 398522

Directions
Greystones is situated on the A523, the main road through Leek from Macclesfield to Ashbourne. The tearoom is next door to Leek

library which is housed in the green-domed Nicholson Institute — a landmark for miles around.

Opening times
Open all year. Monday, Thursday, Sunday, closed. Tuesday, Wednesday, Friday and Saturday, 10 am– 5pm.

Award
1999 Runner up Top Tea Place Award
1999 Tea Council Award of Excellence

Local Interest:
Leeks is surrounded by wonderful countryside with moors, dales, rivers and reservoirs. The town has many fine buildings, antique shops and galleries, and the parish church has some fine examples of handwork carried out in the 19th century by Leek's celebrated School of Embroidery.

It was the flourishing silk industry that made Leek a wealthy thriving community in the 18th century, and the town is full of fascinating reminders of those days – the cobbled market place, the restored water-powered corn mill by the canal, and the Victorian Nicholson Institute, founded in 1882 by Sir Arthur Nicholson, a successful mill owner who built the library and museum (now the Technical College) for the local residents. It was in the rear garden of Greystones, his gracious late 17th century house in the heart of Leek, that the Institute was built.

Greystones tearoom is housed in the front parlour of the house where dark wood panelling, beams and leaded light windows create a wonderful setting for afternoon tea. The Warrillows have created an atmosphere here that makes visitors feel really welcome and relaxed and they offer a wonderful selection of lunchtime savouries and sought-after home-made cakes and desserts such as the Queen Mother's favourite melting date and walnut sponge topped with cream, treacle tart and ginger preserve cake. *Teas served*: House Blend, Traditional English, Traditional Afternoon Blend, Assam, Darjeeling, Earl Grey, Lady Grey, Ceylon, Yunnan, Lapsang Souchong, Green, Jasmine, Lemon, decaffeinated. *Herbal infusions are also offered.*

ROYAL DOULTON VISITOR CENTRE

Nile Street, Burslem, Stoke-on-Trent
Staffordshire ST6 2AJ
Tel: 01782 292434 Fax: 01782 292424
Website: royal-doulton.co.uk

Directions

Leave the M6 at either Junction 15 or 16 and take the A500 towards Stoke-on-Trent. Leave the A500 at the junction with the A527 and

follow the brown tourist signs for Royal Doulton in Burslem.

Opening times

Open all year except Christmas week.
Monday–Saturday, 9.30 am–5 pm.
Sunday, 10.30 am–4.30 pm.

Local Interest:

Stoke on Trent is the home of several large potteries. Royal Doulton offer factory tours, demonstrations of hand painting, intricate china flower making and gilding, museum and figure collection, and extensive shopping facilities.

The Royal Doulton Visitor Centre is "the home of the Royal Doulton figure" and is located within the Royal Doulton factory. As well as offering refreshment and a relaxing location in which to rest after touring the pottery or watching a demonstration of gilding or hand painting, The Sir Henry Doulton Gallery Restaurant is also the museum of the company's history spanning 180 years. Glass cabinets display nearly 1,500 Doulton figures, early stoneware pieces from the 1830s, Lambeth wares and medal winning exhibits from international exhibitions, as well as plates, cups and teapots that include the well-loved Bunnykins and the first china in space.

The lunch and tea time menu includes soup served with a crusty roll. Staffordshire oatcakes with various savoury fillings, salads, jacket potatoes, hot buttered toast, and all sorts of home made cakes – banana and walnut, date and ginger, tea bread, chocolate fudge cake, lemon meringue pie and lots more. A "High Tea" gives you sandwiches and cakes or a scone, and a "Cream Tea" is served with fruit scones and dairy cream. Everything is served on Royal Doulton fine bone china. *Teas served*: Assam, Darjeeling, English Breakfast, Ceylon, Earl Grey, Royal Albert's Old Country Roses Blend, decaffeinated. *Herbal infusions are also offered.*

WALES
REGIONAL MAP

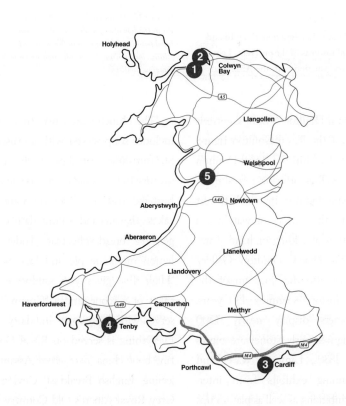

BADGERS

Owners: Barry Mortlock and
Jennie Taylor

The Victoria Shopping Mall
Mostyn Street
Llandudno LL30 2RP
Tel: 01492 871649
Fax: 01492 871974

Directions

From the A55, take the A470 Llandudno link road. When you reach the main shopping High Street, Badgers is situated in the Victorian Shopping Mall directly opposite Marks & Spencer. There is a multi-storey car park above the shopping mall.

Opening times
Open all year. Monday–Saturday,
9.30 am–5 pm. Sunday, 11 am–4 pm.

Local Interest:
The town is home to "Alice in Wonderland" (the house where Alice Liddell was born), the new North Wales Theatre, and old fashioned trams. It is a beautiful Victorian resort with a pier and views of the twin Orme headlands.

Badgers conjures up a Victorian atmosphere with its warm welcome, traditional furniture, tea trolleys, lace curtains and speedy waitresses dressed in neat black dresses, crisp white aprons and white caps. Badgers is often likened to the famous old-fashioned Lyons corner houses because of the girls' "proper" and efficient "Nippy"-like service. The spacious tearoom is elegant and sophisticated inside and relaxingly continental outside where conservatory-style chairs and tables are surrounded by colourful window boxes.

The menu has a very full and appetising variety of traditional treats – cinnamon toast, buttered crumpets, Welsh bara brith, Welsh Rarebit, Scotch Woodcock – hot and cold savouries, a delicious range of home baked morning goods and a mouth watering patisserie are all baked on the premises by resident master bakers (ice mice, dragon eclairs and swan meringues are a must!). The "Traditional Victorian Tea" is the ultimate treat offering you a choice of sandwich , bara brith, fresh baked scone and cake – all served on a Victorian Tiered cake stand. *Teas served*: English Breakfast, Assam, Darjeeling, Ceylon, Earl Grey, Jasmine. *Chamomile Flowers Tisane also offered.*

ST TUDNO HOTEL

Owners: Martin and Janette Bland

Promenade, Llandudno
Gwynedd LL30 2LP
Tel: 01492 874411 Fax: 01492 860407
Website: www.st-tudno.co.uk

Directions
From the A55 take the A470 Llandudno
Link road. On reaching the Promenade,
drive towards the Great Orme headland. The

hotel is directly opposite the pier entrance and
ornamental gardens.

Opening times
Open all year, 7 am–11 pm.

Award
1996–99 Tea Council Award of Excellence
Egon Ronay recommended

Local Interest:
*The town, with its Victorian pier, gardens and beach, is
ideally located for exploring North Wales. Nearby there
are castles, National Trust properties and the world
famous gardens at Bodnant.*

The St Tudno Hotel enjoys a reputation as one of the most luxurious seaside resort hotels in Great Britain and has won an amazing number of awards over the years. Martin and Janette Bland, with their unique flair for hotel keeping and incredibly high standards, really deserve all the accolades. The hotel interiors are wonderfully glamorous, the staff are extremely attentive and the atmosphere is one of charm and warmth and meticulous care. And an extra item of interest is the fact that Alice Liddell, immortalised by Lewis Carroll as the heroine of Alice in Wonderland, stayed at the St Tudno at the age of eight on her first visit to Llandudno in 1861.

In good weather, take tea on the patio and enjoy outstanding views over the bay. In winter, choose one of three beautifully designed lounges. The menu offers two set teas – the Full Welsh Afternoon Tea with a wide range of sandwiches, scones, Bara Brith, traditional Welsh Cakes and home made cakes, and the De-Luxe Afternoon Tea which includes the full afternoon tea and adds smoked salmon sandwiches, strawberries and cream and a glass of champagne. *Teas served:* House Blend, Assam, Darjeeling, Ceylon, Lapsang Souchong, Earl Grey, Jasmine, Gunpowder, Keemun, English Breakfast, China, Yorkshire Gold Medal and decaffeinated. *Fruit flavoured teas and herbal infusions are also offered.*

GWALIA TEA ROOMS

Operated by: Apple Catering

**The Museum of Welsh Life
St Fagans, Cardiff
CF5 6XB
Tel: 01222 566985
Fax: 01222 566985**

Directions

Take exit 33 off the M4 and follow signs to

The Museum of Welsh Life. The tearooms are within the grounds of the museum.

Opening times

Open all year, six days a week except Christmas Day and Boxing Day, 10 am–4.45 pm. Closed Mondays apart from Bank Holidays.

Local Interest:

The tea shop is within the grounds of the Museum of Welsh Life which has a complete Welsh village with blacksmith, school, old cottages, an old photographer's shop and lots more.

Gwalia Tea Rooms are situated on the first floor of Gwalia Stores, a high class department store that was moved stone by stone from the coal-mining village of Ogmore Vale and meticulously rebuilt within the grounds of The Museum of Welsh Life. The interior, once the corn store, is decorated and furnished in the authentic style of the 1920s, with bentwood chairs, old mirrors, a cut glass screen at one end of the room and old photos of the building in its original setting. To get to the tearoom, you have to pass through the old-fashioned ironmongery downstairs where you can still buy an old tin bath, if you want to. However, you might be more interested in the jams and pickles and other home made goodies.

The tea time menu is as traditional as the shop surroundings and includes, of course, Welsh cakes and Bara Brith, which Mike Morton sends out mail order to people who tried it once and now want more. And custard slices are a regular treat, again following a tradition from the days when Mr Llewellyn, who ran Gwalia Stores back in Ogmore Vale, baked them every Friday. *Teas served:* Darjeeling, Assam, Ceylon, Earl Grey, Lapsang Souchong, Jasmine, Gunpowder, Oolong, Yunnan, Rose Pouchong. *Fruit flavoured teas and herbal infusions are also available.*

CELTIC FARE TEAROOMS

Owner: Mr and Mrs C. Phillips

**Vernon House, St Julians Street
Tenby, Pembrokeshire SA70 7AS
Tel: 01834 845258**

Directions

Take the A478 into Tenby and the Celtic Fare Tearooms is half way down St Julians Street on the left hand side, very close to the Harbour and Castle Beach.

Opening times
Open all year.
Monday–Sunday, 10 am–5.30 pm.

Awards
1993   Tea Council Award of Excellence

Local Interest:
You can walk around the old town walls and visit the 14th century Tudor merchant's house (now run by The National Trust), the museum, lifeboat station and aquarium. Fishing trips go from the harbour and boat trips leave every half hour to Caldey Island which is 20 minutes away and has a Cistercian monastery.

Celtic Fare is a real traditional Welsh tearoom serving home-baked cakes, pastries and savouries of a very high standard. In its first year it won a Tea Council Award of Excellence and deserves to be packed all the time with appreciative, hungry customers.

The attraction starts right at the front door to this eye-catching building where bright hanging baskets surround the pretty door and windows. Inside, there is a feeling of warmth and welcome. The old beams are hung with jugs and teapots, lamps cast a warm glow over the cosy, friendly room and there is a real fire in the Victorian hearth and fresh flowers around the room. The Celtic spirit is heightened by the soothing traditional music playing in the background and the really tempting freshly baked Welsh cakes, hot from the griddle and scones served with lashings of Caldey Island clotted cream and fruity jam.

Light snacks are available all day and you can lunch on Welsh rarebits or Heggarty Pie with crisp bacon topping, or take tea with tangy lemon torte, apple cake and fresh fruit pavlovas. The display on the counter will make it really difficult for you to choose. *Teas served:* House Blend, Earl Grey, Darjeeling, Ceylon, Lapsang Souchong. *Fruit flavoured teas and herbal infusions are also offered.*

THE OLD STATION COFFEE SHOP

Owner: Eileen Minter

Dinas Mawddwy
Machynlleth
Powys SY20 9LS
Tel: 01650 531338

Directions

The A470 (the main North to South Wales road) passes the gate to Meirion Mill by Minllyn Bridge one mile north of the A470

junction with the A458 at Mallwyd. The Old Station Coffee Shop is on the right, inside the gate to the Mill.

Opening times

Open March–mid-November.
Monday–Sunday, 9.30 am–5 pm.
Mid-November–January 3rd, 10.30 am–4 pm.

Awards

Egon Ronay recommended

Local Interest:

Meirion Mill is in what were the old slate dressing sheds. The working looms produce cloth that is for sale in the Mill shop. There are walks and climbs in all directions.

The Old Station stands beneath high conifers at the side of a disused railway line in an area of Wales steeped in legend and history and where King Arthur is said to have fought his last battle at Camlan. See the stone in the mill grounds commemorating this. Visitors may walk for miles to explore the surrounding Dinas Mawddwy mountains and countryside that create the backdrop for the old station building. The original waiting room is now two tearooms that still have the old-fashioned station fireplaces and are furnished with pine chairs, tables and dressers. Outside, on the old platform, there are slate tables, teak benches, fresh flowers and plants in tubs and cascading

baskets, and an old station sign to remind you of the days when steam engines pulled their heavy load of freight and passengers through the breathtaking Welsh scenery.

Eileen's menu is deliciously Welsh, and the cheese scones, the Bara Brith and other cakes are so good that people travel hundreds of miles to taste them. The lunchtime menu offers home made soups, quiches, salads, sandwiches and four different ploughmans. Welsh cakes, other whole cakes, honeys, preserves, ice creams and chocolate to take home. *Teas served:* Indian, Darjeeling, Assam, English Breakfast, Earl Grey, Lady Grey, China, decaffeinated. *Herbal infusions are also available.*

S C O T L A N D
R E G I O N A L   M A P

DUMFRIES
❶ Abbey Cottage Tea Rooms 126

EDINBURGH
❷ The Caledonian Hotel   127

FIFE
❸ Kind Kyttock's Kitchen   128

STRATHCLYDE
❹ Coach House Coffee Shop 129
❺ The Willow Tearoom   130
❻ Willow Tea Rooms   131

ABBEY COTTAGE TEA ROOMS

Owners: Morag McKie and
Jacqui Wilson

**26 Main Street, New Abbey
Dumfries DG2 8BY
Tel: 01387 850377**

Directions
Take the A710 from Dumfries to New Abbey
(the Solway Coast Road). Abbey Cottage is

beside Sweetheart Abbey. The Village Car
Park is behind.

Opening times
Open 1st April–31st October and
weekends to Christmas.
Monday–Sunday, 10 am–5.30 pm. 🚭

Awards
Egon Ronay recommended
1999 Tea Council Award of Excellence

Local Interest:
*Wander around the Abbey ruins and learn the story of
Lady Devorgilla. Also visit the Shambellie House Museum of
Costume and an 18th century water mill that still operates.*

If you take the Solway Coast Road
from Dumfries, you will drive through
some wonderful countryside before you
find yourself in the quiet village of New
Abbey. Here stand the rose-coloured remains of Sweetheart Abbey, built by Lady
Devorgilla in the 13th century in memory
of her husband, John Balliol, with whom
she founded Balliol College, Oxford.

Just across the road from the
medieval ruins, 19th century Abbey
Cottage offers a warm welcome and a
delicious selection of healthy home-made
specialities that are served in a friendly,
caring, non-smoking environment. Morag
McKie and her daughter Jacqui use high-
quality local produce and include low-fat

and vegetarian options on their menu.
Home-made soups, granary breads, Scottish country pâté and tasty sandwiches
or salads are perfect for a light lunch,
while the tea time selection includes
Jacqui's excellent carrot or banana cake,
and plain, wholemeal or fruit scones that
are served with Morag's home-made
jams. In good weather, enjoy your tea in
the garden at the back of the pretty
cottage and before leaving, visit the craft
shop next door to browse amongst the
very attractive range of local pottery,
candles and table wares. *Teas served:*
Traditional Blend, Assam, Darjeeling, Earl
Grey and decaffeinated. *Fruit flavoured
teas and herbal infusions are also offered.*

THE CALEDONIAN HOTEL

General Manager: Edna Mullin

Princes Street
Edinburgh EH1 2AB
Tel: 0131 459 9988
Fax: 0131 225 6632

Directions
The Caledonian is situated at the west end of
Princes Street, adjoining Lothian Road.

Opening times
Open all year.
Afternoon tea is served from 3–5.30 pm.

Awards
1996 & 99 Tea Council Award of Excellence

Local Interest:
Within walking distance lie Edinburgh Castle and other
historic buildings, and Princes Street's main shops. Also
nearby are The National Gallery, the Royal Scottish
Academy for Art, and the nineteenth century watchtower
used by police to catch Burke and Hare.

The "Caley" (the locals' affectionate name for the Caledonian Hotel) occupies a prominent position in one of Scotland's finest streets. The lounge has just been completely refurbished and now welcomes visitors into a rich yellow, gold and red room where mess jackets for the staff add to the traditional theme. The view of Edinburgh Castle from the windows is spectacular and the setting creates an interesting and relaxing location for informal lunches and gracious afternoon teas between shopping and sightseeing. The menu which changes regularly offers a sparkling selection of wonderful sandwiches with truly imaginative fillings and

toppings such as – mozzarella, plum tomatoes and pesto, Angus minute steak with mustard and onions, chicken mayonnaise with Swiss cheese and crispy bacon. And the traditional Afternoon Tea consists of finger sandwiches, scones and home made cakes such as Dundee, cherry and Madeira cake. For a special occasion, choose the Celebration Tea with its added glass of Champagne, or simply enjoy a pot of tea and a traditional Scotch pancake. *Teas served:* Breakfast Blend, Assam, Ceylon, Darjeeling, Earl Grey, Lapsang Souchong, Keemun. *Fruit flavoured teas and herbal infusions are also available.*

KIND KYTTOCK'S KITCHEN

Owners: Liz and Bert Dalrymple

Cross Wynd, Falkland
Fife, KY15 7BE
Tel: 01337 857477

Directions
Follow signs from the M90 for Falkland Palace.
Cross Wynd joins the High Street at the
fountain and Mercat Cross.

Opening times
Open all year except Mondays and two weeks
from Christmas Day–January 5th.
Tuesday–Sunday, 10.30 am–5.30 pm.

Awards
1991 & 92   Tea Council Award of Excellence
Egon Ronay recommended
1997 Winner of The Macallan Taste of
Scotland Best Tea Room Award

Local Interest:
Falkland Palace, at the centre of the village, was
built by James IV in the 16th century. The gardens and
tennis court – one of the oldest in Britain – are well
worth a visit.

Kind Kyttock was the heroine of a poem by William Dunbar, the early Scots poet. 'The Ballad of Kind Kyttock' tells how she settled in Falkland and served good food and drink to weary travellers. Liz and Bert Dalrymple, who came here from Glasgow 25 years ago to find a more peaceful life, follow her example and offer tasty traditional Scottish fare in a relaxed atmosphere to thousands of visitors every year from all over the world. In fact, a group of Americans arrived one day with a cutting from the *Los Angeles Times* giving a very positive review of Kind Kyttock's, so news of how good it is has obviously spread far and wide.

The menu has an appealing Scottish flavour – Midlothian oatcakes served with cheddar cheese, Scottish pancakes with cream and home made apricot jam or fresh fruit, traditional Cloutie Dumpling with cream, and an irresistible Rob Roy ice cream with butterscotch sauce and petticoat tail shortbread. All these good things are served in two rooms, upstairs and down, where dark furniture, colourful tablecloths and an interesting selection of prints and paintings on the walls create a very pleasing, old-fashioned atmosphere. *Teas served:* House Blend, Darjeeling, Earl Grey, China, Ceylon, Assam, Russian. *Herbal infusions are also offered.*

COACH HOUSE COFFEE SHOP

Owners: Rowena and Gary Groves

Luss, Loch Lomond
Argyll, Scotland
G83 8NN
Tel: 01436 860341
Fax: 01436 860336
E-mail: coachhouse@lochlomondtrading.
fsnet.co.uk
Website:www.lochlomondtrading.co.uk

Directions
Follow signs to Luss from the A82 (Glasgow to Crianlarich). In Luss, park in the car park and walk towards the centre of the village. The coffee shop is next to the church. 🚭 ♿

Opening times
Open all year except Christmas Day.
In winter, every day, 10 am–5 pm.
In summer, every day, 10 am–6 pm.

Local Interest:
This is a most beautiful area of hills, forests and parkland set around Loch Lomond. On the opposite side of the Loch is the Queen Elizabeth Forest and Ben Lomond.

The genuine Scottish atmosphere of the Coach House in Luss makes it a really wonderful experience for both locals and tourists. The setting is perfect – a Grade I conservation village, the beautiful countryside around Loch Lomond – and inside the shop, the foyer displays a range of exclusive Scottish merchandise, and the coach house décor includes Harris tweed drapes, hand-painted tartan crockery, an open log fire, and a sofa with a warning not to wake guests who may have fallen into a doze after indulging in too many of Rowena's home-baked cakes. With Gary in his kilt and a menu that reflects the locality (with such treats as skeachan fruit cake,

whisky cake, and stokies – traditional soft bread rolls – filled with mature Scottish cheddar or egg mayonnaise made with eggs from the Groves free range Black Rock hens), the Scottish theme runs throughout. Despite its name, the coffee house serves an excellent variety of teas and tea-time traditionals – scones, cinnamon toast, shortbreads, muffins – as well as more robust Scottish lunch time fillers including haggis with neeps and tatties. *Teas served:* Famous Edinburgh, Darjeeling, Lapsang Souchong, Earl Grey, Assam, China, Keemun, Gunpowder, Sri Lanka, Ceylon. *Fruit and herbal infusions are also offered.*

THE WILLOW TEAROOM

Owner: Anne Mulhern

217 Sauchiehall Street
Glasgow G2 3EX
Tel: 0141 332 0521

Directions
The tearoom is on the first floor above
Henderson the jewellers.

Opening times
Open all year.
Monday–Saturday, 9.30 am–4.30 pm.
Sunday, 12 noon–4 pm.

Awards
Egon Ronay recommended

Local Interest:
*Within walking distance of the tearoom is the Glasgow
School of Art, the Tenement House (a reconstruction of a
typical Glaswegian tenement block with original domestic
interiors), the Glasgow Concert Hall and the Kelvin Grove
Museum. There are also many other examples of
Mackintosh architecture.*

While tea shops often manage to create an impression of past times, The Willow Tearoom is a genuine example of turn-of-the-century design. The Room de Luxe is the only remaining room of Miss Kate Cranston's 'tearoom empire', created for her by Charles Rennie Mackintosh in 1904. His wonderful Arts and Crafts style that heralded Art Deco, gave his architecture, furniture, lamps and tableware the strong rectilinear contours and geometric shapes that fascinate the eye. Mackintosh had previously designed the interior for three other Cranston tearooms, but the Willow allowed him to style the exterior and interior of an entire building.

In 1983, the tearoom was restored by the current owner, Anne Mulhern. The mirror friezes, the gesso panel and the ornate leaded doors had happily survived and the chairs and tables were reproduced to Mackintosh's original 1904 design. An unhurried atmosphere matches the elegance of the interior and the comprehensive list of teas, favourite tea time traditionals and cakes makes this a very special experience. *Teas served:* Tearoom Blend, Breakfast, Earl Grey, Lapsang Souchong, Darjeeling, Ceylon, Assam, Rose Petal, Keemun, Jasmine Blossom, Yunnan, Kenya, Rose Pouchong, decaffeinated. *Fruit flavoured teas and herbal infusions are also offered.*

WILLOW TEA ROOMS

Owner: Anne Mulhern

97 Buchanan Street
Glasgow G1 3HF
Tel: 0141 204 5242
Fax: 0141 204 5242

Directions

Buchanan Street is in the city centre, just round the corner from both Queen Street Station and Central Station. Willow Tea Rooms is on the section of Buchanan Street that runs from Argyle Street to St Vincent Place.

Opening times
Open all year. Monday–Saturday, 8.30 am–5.30 pm. Sunday, 12 noon–5 pm.

Local Interest:
Glasgow is famous for its Charles Rennie Mackintosh architecture, and a wide variety of museums, theatres and galleries that house collections of French Impressionist paintings, medieval tapestries, and Chinese art.

In July 1997, Anne Mulhern opened this new shop immediately next door to what was once Kate Cranston's original Buchanan Street Tea Rooms. This shop was Charles Rennie Mackintosh's first involvement in Miss Cranston's once famous chain of tearooms. His work there was limited to wall murals, but he went on to design several other rooms for her. This new property contains recreations of the White Dining Room which he created for her Ingram Street shop in 1900, and the intensely blue Chinese Room which he designed for the same premises in 1911. Anybody who enjoys Mackintosh design and architecture will love the style of both rooms where Anne has lovingly recreated the atmosphere of a bygone age.

The menu has a strong Scottish emphasis. Scottish Farmhouse Cheddar cheese tops jacket potatoes and drizzles from toasted sandwiches; Scottish smoked salmon fills sandwiches, croissants and bagels or accompanies scrambled eggs or smoked trout; Arbroath Smokies are served with lemon and hot buttered toast; and the cakes and desserts include Scottish shortbread and traditional cloutie dumpling. *Teas served*: Assam, Ceylon, Darjeeling, Earl Grey, English Breakfast, Gunpowder, Jasmine, Keemun, Kenya, Lapsang Souchong, Rose Petal, Russian Caravan, Tea Room Blend. *Herbal infusions are also offered.*

TEA ROOMS AROUND THE WORLD

Because many countries around the globe do not regularly drink tea and do not normally offer it on everyday menus, travelling outside the UK on holiday or business can mean having to miss out on good cups of tea. Many British travellers always pack a supply of their favourite tea in their suitcase or overnight bag so that they can at least start the day with a familiar brew. But what about while they're out sightseeing, shopping, on their way to and from meetings, or entertaining foreign friends. It's usually relatively easy to find somewhere to go for coffee, a beer or a glass of wine, but when it comes to a cup of tea, it's a different story.

To help readers find those elusive cups of tea outside the UK, the Guild of Tea Shops Guide Book is now including a section that recommends a few of the best tearooms and tea lounges around the world. As interest in tea has grown globally over the past few years, so more and more people have opened quality tea rooms, and more and more hotels have started offering a comprehensive tea list as part of their menu – particularly in Japan and the United States. As the Guild discovers more suitable places that match up to its high standards, so this section of the book will grow. We are starting this year with venues in Japan, the US and France, and hope in the future to be able to help tea lovers find excellent cups of tea in other European countries and elsewhere around the world.

MARIAGE FRÈRES

Mariage Frères have 3 shops at the following addresses

Mariage Frères Le Marais
30 rue du Bourg-Tibourg
75004 Paris
Tel: (+33) (1) 42 72 28 11   Fax: (+33) (1) 42 74 51 68

Directions

Take the metro to Saint-Paul. Take rue de Rivoli, then turn right into rue du Bourg-Tibourg.

Mariage Frères Rive Gauche
13 rue des Grands Augustins
75006 Paris
Tel: (+33) (1) 40 51 82 50   Fax: (+33) (1) 44 07 07 52

Directions

Take the metro to Saint-Michel. Take rue Saint-André des Arts, then turn right into rue des Grands Augustins.

Mariage Frères Etoile
260 rue du Faubourg-Saint-Honoré
75008 Paris
Tel: (+33) (1) 46 22 18 54   Fax: (+33) (1) 42 67 18 54

Directions

Take the metro to Ternes. Turn left into rue du Faubourg-Saint-Honoré.

Opening times

Opening times for all three shops are the same.
Open all year.
The shops are open Monday–Sunday, 10.30am–7.30 pm.
The tearooms are open 12 noon–7 pm.

Mariage Frère's links with tea began in the mid-17th century, when Nicolas Mariage travelled to the Orient on behalf of Louis XIV and the French East India Company, while his brother Pierre made voyages to Madagascar, also as special envoy for the East India Company. During the 18th century, Jean-François Mariage was still trading teas and spices, a business that was carried on by his sons. The present company was established by Jean-François' grandsons, Henri and Edouard, in 1854 and is today the oldest tea importer in France. Tea lovers can choose from the list of more than 400 teas from all over the world in the three Parisien Mariage Frères 'salons de thé', in several shops in Tokyo, Japan, on the fourth floor of Dickens and Jones in London, at 'T' Salon in New York City, or by mail order.

Any visitor to Paris should make a special point of taking tea at one of the salons – they are absolutely not to be missed. The original shop in the Marais has a classic colonial feel with elegant palms, calm relaxing neutral colours and gracious staff who look after guests with impeccable care and attention. The first floor tearoom in the shop on the Rive Gauche, opened in 1990, and the newest Etoile tearoom, opened in 1997, are both very similar in their period elegance and charm and serve the same wonderful gâteaux, tortes and tartes and the same selection of fine teas. These are world emporia of tea. You can choose Black, Green, White, Oolong, Pu'erh, compressed or flavoured teas from India, Sri Lanka, China, Taiwan, Japan, Korea, Bangladesh, Nepal, Indonesia, Vietnam, Russia, Turkey, Iran, Argentina, Brazil, Cameroon, Kenya, Zimbabwe, Rwanda, South Africa and more – in fact from any of the thirty or so tea producing areas of the world. The list changes from time to time with the changing quality of teas from different gardens and estates each year, but for example, if you wish to drink a Darjeeling, you will have a choice of approximately 18 first flush, 20 second flush, and several Darjeeling blends. If China black is your preference, there are teas from Yunnan, Anhui, Szechwan and Fujian. And if you prefer Earl Grey, Mariage usually offer about 12 different blends ranging through Imperial, Silver Tip, Oolong,

Green, Decaffeinated, English, and Smoky varieties.

Once you have chosen your particular leaf (with, if necessary, the help and advice of the waiter), a great deal of attention goes into the actual brewing of your tea. It is not simply a question here of putting leaves into a pot, pouring on some boiling water and delivering the pot to the table. At Mariage, the leaves are carefully measured, the brewing time is calculated and timed, and the water temperature is checked before the infused tea is decanted into a clean pot and delivered to your table. So, what each guest enjoys is a perfect liquor in which there are no leaves that can become bitter by over-brewing. And to ensure that different flavoured leaves do not contaminate and spoil your tea, scented teas are served in colour-coded pots. Everything is done with such care and style here and the shops attract tea lovers and connoisseurs from Paris and beyond.

After sampling one of the fabulous teas, don't miss the retail counters in each of the shops. They are almost like museums with unusual tea pots and brewing equipment, books, tea caddies, compressed teas, tea jellys and tea-scented candles. The teas themselves are stored in beautiful old-fashioned large black caddies, each sitting in its own niche in the bank of shelves against the wall. How to choose? Take your time and ask for help. All the staff really do know what they are selling and are delighted to explain and offer advice before you buy for yourself or select gifts to take home to friends.

And the shops do in fact each have a little museum which offer a fascinating insight into the history of tea and tea brewing with their collections of rare brewing equipage, antique caddies, and teapots and teacups of all styles from ancient Chinese to 20th century art deco. Whatever you do, if you are in Paris, don't miss Mariage Frères. Each shop is an absolute gem. *Teas served:* 450 fine loose leaf teas from all world tea regions.

ELMWOOD INN

Owners: Bruce and Shelly Richardson

205 East Fourth Street
Perryville, Kentucky 40468
USA
Tel: (001) (606) 332 2400
E-mail: tea@elmwoodinn.com
Website: www. elmwoodinn.com

Directions
Elmwood Inn is located 90 minutes south east of Louisville and 60 minutes south west of Lexington.

Opening times
Open all year on Thursday, Friday, Saturday.
Seating at 1 pm and 3 pm.

Elmwood Inn was built in 1842 for a local merchant by the name of Burton, and the general village store that he ran still stands on the other side of the river. During the Civil War, the house served as a hospice for wounded soldiers from the 1862 Battle of Perryville, then from 1896 until 1924 it became Elmwood Academy. Later, it was turned into a restaurant and then fell into disrepair and stood totally neglected until the spring of 1900, when the Richardsons bought the derelict building and spent the next few years restoring it to its period charm. Once all the hard work was finished, they initially ran the house as a bed and breakfast as well as a stylish tea venue, but when teas became by far the most important part of their activities, Bruce and Shelly started concentrating totally on that side of the

business. At first Shelly baked all the cakes and scones herself but now employs skilled and aptly-named pastry chef, Debbie Wheat, to create the wonderful selection of sweet and savoury afternoon tea delicacies.

Elmwood has ten tables in the dining room, library and garden, and it is best to book ahead as available places are rapidly reserved by guests who drive or fly in from California or New England to sample the delicious four course tea. The menu changes each month and is themed to the season or to a particular festivity. So April brings Shakespeare Tea with Merchant Tea Sandwich, English Garden Sandwich, Juliet's Sand Bars and Titania's Fairy cake; in August guests are served the Sunflower Tea with sunflower wholewheat scones, Blueberry Bars, Summer Cake and nectarine sorbet; while the Kentucky Harvest Tea serves you Shaker Lemon Tarts, traditional Chocolate Bourbon Balls, Country Ham Pate with corn muffins and Elmwood Inn Woodford Pudding with Blackberry Brandy sauce. Each menu suggests a suitable tea to compliment the sandwiches and desserts, but there is also a comprehensive list of teas to choose from.

Both Shelly and Bruce Richardson hold degrees in music and share a passion for the arts, and have brought an added cultural dimension to Elmwood Inn. Each month they display the work of different Kentucky artists, while the music that plays during afternoon tea is carefully chosen to reflect the time of year, special event or to enhance the theme of the meal being served. The diary of events also includes live performances by local string quartets, brass bands, pianists or singers, and 'Plein Air' painting with artists working on the lawn. The blend of sensations at Elmwood is really very special. It has been said the "the mixture of tea, beautiful foods, gardens, art and music feeds the soul as well as the body at the Elmwood Inn. You taste first with your eyes at this sanctuary for the spirit". And, in the Richardsons' own words, "Tea is about conversation and taking time for the beautiful things in life – the whole culture of tea is what entices people". The Richardsons have recently started offering training courses for existing and potential tearoom owners and also organise group visits to Britain for American tea lovers.

Elmwood Inn also has two gift shops where visitors can buy packages of tea, home-made lemon or cranberry curd, scone mix, shortbread mix, cookies, gourmet sugar cubes decorated with tiny sugar flowers and teacups, and copies of the three books that the Richardsons have written – A Year of Teas at the Elmwood Inn, A Tea For All Seasons, and The Great Tea Rooms of Britain.

Teas served and offered for sale: Traditional English Breakfast, Darjeeling, Irish Blend, Mayor's Cup, Kentucky Blend, Earl Grey, Lapsang Souchong, Keemun, China Oolong, Gunpowder, Jasmine, orange and spice, raspberry, apricot, peach, rose, wild cherry, black currant.

BARAKURA ENGLISH GARDEN

The Japanese company, Barakura English Garden, has joined forces with three other Japanese companies to establish a chain of extremely attractive traditional English-style shops, gardens and tearooms. The company's 'Original Teas' are being marketed in co-operation with The UK Tea Council and St James's Teas of London.

The philosophy behind the tea concept comes from the President of Barakura English Garden, Eugène Yamada, and the Original Teas are selected from the best tea gardens of the year. Yamada says that this approach will bring about a 'tea revolution' in Japan.

The tea served at all the Barakura English Gardens are: Assam, Darjeeling and Earl Grey. *Camomile, Peppermint and Lemon Grass herbal infusions are also offered on the menus.*

IKSPIARI BARAKURA ENGLISH GARDEN

Owners: Ikspiari Company Ltd

Maihama, Urayasu-City, Chiba Prefecture, Japan

Directions **Ikspiari is in front of Maihama Station on the JR Keiyo-Line. Barakura English Garden is on Museum Lane.**

Opening times **Open all year. Monday–Sunday, 10 am–10 pm.**

Maihama-City is beside Tokyo Bay which is currently being developed as a resort with hotels and major leisure facilities. By July 2000, Ikspiari will be up and running as a large shopping centre with the unique theme of a town full of entertainment and history. Barakura English Garden, just one amongst more than a hundred shops, is set out like a classic English manor house and offers a very attractive range of plants, seeds, gardening products, original ladies' clothing and gifts from England. This is Barakura's biggest shop and is run in co-operation with Ikspiari Co. Ltd. The tearoom serves Barakura's original teas, a selection of pastries and traditional British foods from Chatsworth Farm Shop in Derbyshire. *Teas served:* Assam, Darjeeling and Earl Grey. *Herbal infusions are also offered.*

TATESHIHA HEIGHTS

BARAKURA ENGLISH GARDEN

Owners: The Yamada Family

5047 Kuridaira Kitayama
Chino-City
Nagano Prefecture
391-0301 Japan
Tel: (+81) (0) 266 77 2019
Website: www.barakura.co.jp

Directions
The Garden is just off the Chyuo-Highway at No 20 Suwa IC. Continue for about 20 minutes along this road, called Venus Line, which leads to Utukushigahara-heights.

Opening times
Open all year except in the snow season. In summer, Monday–Sunday, 9 am–6 pm. In winter, Monday–Sunday, 9.30 am–5 pm. Please telephone to confirm opening times.

The Tateshiha area is famous as one of the most popular resorts in Japan with features not dissimilar from England's Lake District. In the summer, visitors enjoy the beautiful mountains and lakes and in winter, the attractions include hot springs and skiing.

In 1990, the Yamada family of Kowa Creative Art Company Limited created Barakura English Garden at Tateshiha Heights. It was the first authentic English-style garden in Japan and had a totally English workforce. Mr Kay Yamada, a well-known horticulturalist who has been introducing English culture to the Japanese for ten years, was responsible for that first garden and for the Japanese boom in interest in English gardens and gardening that followed.

Visitors to Tateshiha Heights can enjoy English afternoon tea on the terrace in the garden. The menu offers pastries and English country style meals prepared by two French chefs. Chatsworth Farm Shop foods are also available.

Teas served: Assam, Darjeeling and Earl Grey. *Herbal infusions are also offered.*

DAIMARU SHINSAIBASHI

BARAKURA ENGLISH GARDEN

Owners: Daimaru Shinsaibashi
Company Limited

1-7-1 Shinsaibashi-suji
Osaka-City
Osaka Prefecture
542-8501 Japan
Tel: (+81) (0) 6 6271 1231

Directions

The Daimaru Shinsaibashi department store is near Shinsaibashi Station on the subway Midosuji-Line to Nakamozu. The Barakura English Garden is on the rooftop.

Opening times

Open all year.
Monday–Sunday, 10 am–7.30 pm.
Please telephone to confirm opening times.

Osaka has been Japan's second busiest city for 400 years. People in Osaka are well known as gourmets.

On 25th March 2000, the project to create three English gardens, a garden shop and a Tea Restaurant on the roof of the Daimaru Shinsaibashi department store was realised in co-operation between Barakura English Garden and Daimaru Shinsaibashi Co. Ltd. In response to a request from Daimaru, Mr Eugene Yamada, President of Barakura,

co-ordinated the details and Robert Adam designed the structure in keeping with the department stores early 20th century Art Deco style.

The Tea Restaurant here was the first to serve and sell Barakura's 'Original Teas'. The theme is healthy eating and several of the dishes on the menu are made using British food products.

Teas served: Assam, Darjeeling and Earl Grey. *Herbal infusions are also offered.*

A member of The Tea Council

The Tea Council

Guild of Tea Shops

INDEX OF THE BEST TEA PLACES

ENGLAND

WALES

SCOTLAND

AROUND THE WORLD

LEADING UK TEA SUPPLIERS

UK Blenders & Packers
Ahmad Tea Ltd
Brodie Melrose Drysdale & Co Ltd
Burnham Trading Co Ltd
D J Miles & Co
Finlays Ltd
Gala Coffee & Tea Ltd
George Payne & Co Ltd
Imporient (UK) Ltd
Kamet Ltd
Keith Spicer & Co Ltd
Langdons (Coffee & Tea) Ltd
London & Scottish International Ltd
Matthew Algie & Co Ltd
Nambarrie Tea Ltd
Nairobi Coffee & Tea Co Ltd
Netherbourne Foods Ltd
Newby Teas
New English Teas Ltd

Norfolk Tea & Coffee Co
Northern Tea Merchants
Premier Beverages
  Glengettie Tea Co Ltd
  London Herb & Spice Co Ltd
  Melroses Ltd
  Ridgways
Ringtons Ltd
R Twining & Co Ltd
  Jacksons of Piccadilly Ltd
  Nambarrie Ltd
Samuel Kaye & Son Ltd
Taylors of Harrogate
Tetley GB Ltd
Van den Bergh Foods Ltd
Whittard of Chelsea Ltd
Williamson & Magor Ltd
Windmill Tea & Coffee Ltd

A member of The Tea Council

The Tea Council

Guild of Tea Shops